Songs for Primaries

COMPILED AND EDITED BY

Nettie Lou Jones & Saxe Adams

Illustrated by James Padgett

BROADMAN PRESS ● Nashville, Tennessee

Contents

INDEXES

Preface

Singing is a happy and wonderful experience in the life of a child. Children sing spontaneously and naturally whether at home, church, or school. Songs they love to sing can be a constant source of pleasure and satisfaction to them. Sometimes singing is the easiest way for children to express their true feelings. One of the first ways they give expression to their praise and worship of God is by singing.

Songs for Primaries is designed to enrich the lives of boys and girls, ages six, seven, and eight. The varying needs and interests of children have been kept in mind in the selection of this material. These songs, grouped by church-related topics, will help the children grow in their relationship to God, to Jesus, to the Bible, to their church, to others, to home and family, and to themselves.

The music of these songs lies within the singing range for these boys and girls. The tunes, which are singable and pleasing, represent the rich heritage of Christian song. Along with familiar songs in these pages will be found new tunes and new texts, as well as new tunes for familiar texts. A number of songs appear here for the first time. A few selections from *Songs for 4's and 5's* have been included as transitional material so that all the songs will not be entirely strange to the newly arrived six-year-old.

A fine selection of hymns common to congregational usage has been included. These hymns will begin to acquaint the child with the wonderful literature of congregational song he will sing in coming years. In the selection of these hymns, careful study has been given to the choice of stanzas appropriate to this age group. In some instances, simple accompaniments have been provided to give more prominence to the melodic line.

Autoharp markings appear on many of the songs to enable the workers to use this helpful instrument in singing with the children. The instrumental numbers will prove useful for listening music. The rounds offer opportunities for boys and girls to become acquainted with the sound of an additional melody interwoven with their own melody, an excellent beginning for part singing. The fun and folk song section provides songs for relaxation. Numerous folk melodies from around the world add worldwide scope to this material.

We are grateful to those who have kindly granted permission for the use of copyrighted materials. Every effort has been made to acknowledge ownership of copyrights throughout this collection. If, inadvertently, some error has occurred in this regard, correction will be made in future printings.

Genuine appreciation is expressed to LaVerne Ashby, Dolores Baker, Robert Dowdy, Abbie Louise Green, Doris Monroe, and Elsie Rives for their untiring efforts in assisting with the compilation of this book. Their keen interest and helpful suggestions have been of invaluable aid.

Nettie Lou Jones
Saxe Adams

PRAISING GOD

O Praise Ye the Lord　　　　　　　1

From Psalm 150　　　　　　　　　　　Arr. from CESAR FRANCK

1. O praise ye the Lord, Praise Him in His tem - ple!
2. O praise ye the Lord, Praise Him on the trum - pet!
3. With cym - bals and drum, And tim - brels and or - gan,

O praise ye the Lord, Praise Him for His might - y acts!
O praise ye the Lord, Praise Him with a joy - ful song!
Let all things that breathe In mu - sic O praise the Lord!

Sing to God in Joyful Voice

VIRGINIA C. MURDOCK

Spanish Hymn Melody

Sing to God in joy-ful voice, In His lov-ing hand re-joice.

Earth and sky a-like pro-claim Prais-es to His ho-ly name.

He who guides the swal-lows' flight Will not lose thee from His sight;

All thy trust in Him con-fide, Ev-er in His love a-bide.

O Come, Let Us Sing unto the Lord

(Antiphonal)

Psalm 95: 1a

EVELYN M. PHILLIPS

O come, let us sing un-to the Lord,

O come, let us sing un-to the Lord,

Sing prais - es, sing prais - es,

O come, let us sing un-to the Lord.

4
Praise to God for Seeing

MATILDA M. PENSTONE

ETHEL V. WILLIAMS

Praise to God for things we see; The grow - ing flow'r, the wav - ing tree, Our moth-er's face, the clear blue sky, Where birds and clouds go float-ing by. Praise to God for see - ing!

5
Rejoice, Rejoice

EDWARD H. PLUMPTRE

ARTHUR H. MESSITER

Re-joice, re-joice, Re-joice, give thanks and sing.
Re-joice, re-joice,

JOHN J. MOMENT

Ancient Hebrew Melody
Arr. by MAX LYALL

Men and chil-dren ev-'ry-where With sweet mu-sic fill the air! Na-tions, come, your voic-es raise To the Lord in hymns of praise! Join the an-gel song, All the worlds to Him be-long! Ho-ly, ho-ly, To our God all glo-ry be!

7   I Will Sing Praise

Psalm 9: 1; 18: 1; 105: 1

NORA B. STUCKER

1. I will sing praise to God, I will sing praise to God,
2. I will love Thee, O God, I will love Thee, O God,
3. I will thank Thee, O God, I will thank Thee, O God,

I will praise Him, I will praise Him, I will sing praise to God.
I will love Thee, I will love Thee, I will love Thee, O God.
I will thank Thee, I will thank Thee, I will thank Thee, O God.

8   Sing to God

AURORA M. SHUMATE, stanza 1
SUSAN BAKER, stanza 2

IDA T. TRUSS

1. Sing to God, sing prais - es, Sing to God, sing prais - es,
2. Sing to God, be joy - ful, Sing to God, be joy - ful,

Sing to God, sing to God, Sing to God, sing prais - es.
Sing to God, sing to God, Sing to God, be joy - ful.

Hallelujah!

From the Hebrew
By IRVING WOLFE

Hebrew Folk Song
Acc. by JOHANA HARRIS

Hal - le - lu - jah, Hal - le - lu - jah! Sing praise un - to the Lord; Hal - le - lu - jah, Hal - le - lu - jah! All praise with one ac - cord. High sound - ing cym - bals, ev - 'ry voice, Hal - le - lu - jah, Hal - le - lu - jah! All that have breath, in Him re - joice, Hal - le - lu - jah, Hal - le - lu - jah!

10   O Sing unto the Lord

From Psalm 98

MARGARET BAKER

O sing un-to the Lord a new song;

Re - joice, re - joice and sing praise.

11   All That Has Life and Breath
(From *Hymn of Praise*)

FELIX MENDELSSOHN

FELIX MENDELSSOHN
Arr. by WILLIAM J. REYNOLDS

All that has life and breath, Sing to the Lord,

Hal - le - lu - jah, Sing to the Lord.

Come with Hearts Rejoicing

12

LINA A. RAUSCHENBERG

From BEETHOVEN, Opus 61
LINA A. RAUSCHENBERG, alt.

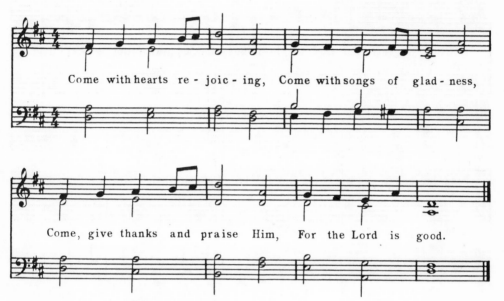

Come with hearts re - joic - ing, Come with songs of glad - ness,

Come, give thanks and praise Him, For the Lord is good.

Great Is the Lord

13

Psalm 145: 3

LEE RODGERS

Great is the Lord And great - ly to be praised,

Great is the Lord And great - ly to be praised.

14 God Is Great and God Is Glorious

MABEL DOLLAR

GERALDINE E. MUCHMORE

God is great and God is glo-ri-ous; Let us praise Him ev-'ry day!

Sing-ing songs and work-ing joy-ful-ly, Let us praise Him ev-'ry day!

God is great and God is glo-ri-ous; Let us praise Him ev-'ry day!

15 Hosanna!

Unknown

Unknown

Ho-san - na! Ho-san - na! The lit-tle chil-dren sing.

Ho-san - na! Ho-san - na! For Christ, the Lord, is King.

Doxology

THOMAS KEN

From the *Genevan Psalter*, 1551

Praise God from whom all bless - ings flow; Praise

Him all crea - tures here be - low; Praise Him a - bove, ye

heav'n - ly host; Praise Fa - ther, Son, and Ho - ly Ghost. A - MEN.

17 All Things Bright and Beautiful

CECIL F. ALEXANDER

Ad. from LOUIS SPOHR

1. All things bright and beau-ti-ful, All things great and small,
2. Cold wind in the win-ter, Pleas-ant sum-mer sun,

All things wise and won-der-ful; Our Fa-ther made them all.
Ripe fruits in the gar-den; He made them ev-'ry one.

Each lit-tle flow'r that o-pens, Each lit-tle bird that sings;
He gave us eyes to see them, And lips that we might tell

He made their glow-ing col-ors, He made their ti-ny wings.
How good is God our Fa-ther Who do-eth all things well.

With Happy Voices Ringing

WILLIAM G. TARRANT

BERTHOLD TOURS

1. With hap-py voic-es ring-ing, Thy chil-dren, Lord, ap-pear; Their joy-ous prais-es bring-ing In an-thems full and clear; For skies of gold-en splen-dor, For az-ure roll-ing sea, For blos-soms sweet and ten-der, O Lord, we wor-ship Thee.

2. For though no eye be-holds Thee, No hand Thy touch may feel, Thy u-ni-verse un-folds Thee, Thy star-ry heav'ns re-veal; The earth and all its glo-ry, Our homes and all we love Tell forth the won-drous sto-ry Of One who reigns a-bove.

Saviour, Teach Me Day by Day

JANE E. LEESON

From *The Parish Choir,* 1850

1. Sav - iour, teach me day by day
2. With a child's glad heart of love
3. Teach me thus Thy steps to trace,
4. Thus may I re - joice to show

Love's sweet les - son to o - bey;
At Thy bid - ding may I move,
Strong to fol - low in Thy grace,
That I feel the love I owe;

Sweet - er les - son can - not be,
Prompt to serve and fol - low Thee,
Learn - ing how to love from Thee,
Sing - ing, till Thy face I see,

Lov - ing Him who first loved me.
Lov - ing Him who first loved me.
Lov - ing Him who first loved me.
Of His love who first loved me.

For the Beauty of the Earth

FOLLIOTT S. PIERPOINT

From a Chorale by
CONRAD KOCHER

1. For the beau - ty of the earth, For the glo - ry
2. For the won - der of each hour Of the day and
3. For the joy of hu - man love, Broth - er, sis - ter,
4. For Thy church that ev - er - more Lift - eth ho - ly

of the skies, For the love which from our birth
of the night, Hill and vale, and tree and flow'r,
par - ent, child, Friends on earth, and friends a - bove,
hands a - bove, Of - f'ring up on ev - 'ry shore

O - ver and a - round us lies; Christ our God, to
Sun and moon, and stars of light; Christ our God, to
For all gen - tle thoughts and mild; Christ our God, to
Her pure sac - ri - fice of love; Christ our God, to

Thee we raise This our hymn of grate - ful praise.
Thee we raise This our hymn of grate - ful praise.
Thee we raise This our hymn of grate - ful praise.
Thee we raise This our hymn of grate - ful praise.

21   "Hosanna!" Be the Children's Song

JAMES MONTGOMERY   From *Gesangbuch der Herzogl,* 1784

1. "Ho-san-na!" be the chil-dren's song To Christ, the
2. "Ho-san-na!" sound from hill to hill, And spread from

chil-dren's King; His praise, to whom they all be-long, Let
plain to plain; While, loud-er, sweet-er, clear-er still, Woods

all the chil-dren sing. "Ho-san-na!" then, our
ech-o to the strain.

REFRAIN

song shall be; "Ho-san-na to our King!" This

is the chil-dren's ju-bi-lee; Let all the chil-dren sing.

Come, Ye Thankful People, Come

HENRY ALFORD

GEORGE J. ELVEY

Come, ye thank - ful peo - ple, come, Raise the song of

har - vest home! All is safe - ly gath - ered in,

Ere the win - ter storms be - gin; God, our Mak - er,

doth pro - vide For our wants to be sup - plied: Come to

God's own tem - ple, come, Raise the song of har - vest home.

23   For All the Blessings of the Year

ALBERT H. HUTCHINSON

ROBERT N. QUAILE

1. For all the bless - ings of the year,
2. For life and health, those com - mon things,

For all the friends we hold so dear, For peace on
Which ev - 'ry day and hour brings, For home, where

earth, both far and near, We thank Thee, Lord.
our af - fec - tion clings, We thank Thee, Lord.

24   Praise Him, All Ye Little Children

Anonymous

CAREY BONNER

1. Praise Him, praise Him, all ye lit - tle chil - dren, God is love, God is love;
2. Love Him, love Him, all ye lit - tle chil - dren, God is love, God is love;
3. Thank Him, thank Him, all ye lit - tle chil - dren, God is love, God is love;

Praise Him, praise Him, all ye lit-tle chil-dren, God is love, God is love.
Love Him, love Him, all ye lit-tle chil-dren, God is love, God is love.
Thank Him, thank Him, all ye lit-tle chil-dren, God is love, God is love.

When Morning Gilds the Skies 25

From the German, *c.* 1800
Tr. by EDWARD CASWALL

JOSEPH BARNBY

1. When morn-ing gilds the skies, My heart a-wak-ing cries,
2. When-e'er the sweet church bell Peals o-ver hill and dell,

May Je-sus Christ be praised! A-like at work and prayer,
May Je-sus Christ be praised! O hark to what it sings,

To Je-sus I re-pair; May Je-sus Christ be praised.
As joy-ous-ly it rings, May Je-sus Christ be praised.

26   All Creatures of Our God and King

FRANCIS OF ASSISI
Tr. by WILLIAM A. DRAPER

Melody from *Geistliche Kirchengesang*, 1623
Arr. by MAX LYALL

1. All crea-tures of our God and King, Lift
2. Thou rush-ing wind that art so strong, Ye

up your voice and with us sing Al-le-lu-ia! Al-le-lu-ia!
clouds that sail in heav'n a-long, O praise Him! Al-le-lu-ia!

Thou burn-ing sun with gold-en beam, Thou sil-ver moon with
Thou ris-ing morn, in praise re-joice, Ye lights of eve-ning,

soft-er gleam! O praise Him, O praise Him! Al-le-
find a voice! O praise Him, O praise Him! Al-le-

lu-ia! Al-le-lu-ia! Al-le-lu - ia!
lu-ia! Al-le-lu-ia! Al-le-lu - ia!

MALTBIE D. BABCOCK   FRANKLIN L. SHEPPARD

1. This is my Fa-ther's world, And to my
2. This is my Fa-ther's world, The birds their

lis - t'ning ears, All na - ture sings, and round me rings
car - ols raise; The morn - ing light, the lil - y white

The mu - sic of the spheres. This is my Fa-ther's
De - clare their Ma - ker's praise. This is my Fa-ther's

world, I rest me in the thought Of rocks and trees,
world, He shines in all that's fair; In the rust - ling grass

of skies and seas; His hand the won - ders wrought.
I hear him pass, He speaks to me ev - 'ry - where.

28   Come, Thou Almighty King

Anonymous

FELICE DE GIARDINI

Come, Thou Al - might - y King, Help us Thy name to sing,

Help us to praise: Fa - ther! all - glo - ri - ous, O'er all vic -

to - ri - ous, Come, and reign o - ver us, An - cient of Days.

29   I Am So Glad

PHILIP P. BLISS

PHILIP P. BLISS

I am so glad that Je-sus loves me, Je-sus loves me, Je-sus loves me,

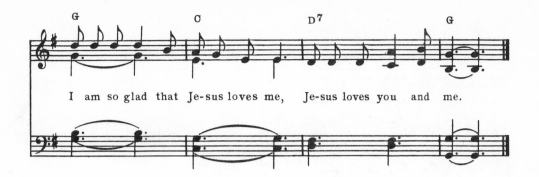

I am so glad that Je-sus loves me, Je-sus loves you and me.

Fairest Lord Jesus

From the German, Seventeenth Century

From *Schlesische Volkslieder*, 1842
Arr. by RICHARD S. WILLIS

Fair - est Lord Je - sus, Rul - er of all na - ture,

O Thou of God and man the Son; Thee will I cher - ish,

Thee will I hon - or, Thou, my soul's glo-ry, joy and crown.

31 O My Soul, Bless God the Father

From Psalm 103
United Presbyterian *Book of Psalms,* 1871

CHRISTIAN F. WITT

1. O my soul, bless God the Fa - ther; All with - in me
2. Bless the Fa - ther, all His crea - tures, Ev - er un - der

bless His name; Bless the Fa - ther, and for - get not
His con - trol, All through-out His vast do - min - ion:

All His mer - cies to pro - claim.
Bless the Fa - ther, O my soul. A - MEN.

32 Thanksgiving Time Has Come

Folk Song

Thanks-giv-ing time has come a-gain, Thank our lov-ing Fa - ther;

Thank Him, thank Him, Thank Him, thank Him, Thank Him for our ★ _____

★ The children may suggest things for which they wish to thank God.

Father, We Thank Thee 33

CLARE GIFFIN

Adapted from J. S. BACH

1. Fa-ther, we thank Thee, Fa-ther, we thank Thee, Thank Thee for
2. Fa-ther, we thank Thee, Fa-ther, we thank Thee, Thank Thee for
3. Fa-ther, we thank Thee, Fa-ther, we thank Thee, Thank Thee for

all that is hap-py and gay! For all our pleas-ures,
all that is gen-tle and kind! For all our near ones,
all that is love-ly and free! Sun-light and flow-ers,

For all our treas-ures, Mu-sic and laugh-ter and games that we play!
For all our dear ones, Playmates and par-ents and friends that we find!
Rainbow and show-ers, Moon-light and star-light and moun-tain and sea!

From *The High Road of Song* by Foresman. Copyright 1931, American Book Company. Used by permission.

34 For the Fruit upon the Tree

MARY MAPES DODGE

W. K. BASSFORD

1. For the fruit up-on the tree, For the birds that
2. For our com-rades and our plays, And our hap-py

sing of Thee, For the earth in beau-ty dressed, Fa-ther,
hol-i-days, For the joy-ful work and true That a

moth-er, and the rest, For Thy pre-cious lov-ing care,
lit-tle child may do, For our lives but just be-gun,

REFRAIN

For Thy boun-ty ev-'ry-where, Fa-ther, we thank Thee;
For the great gift of Thy Son,

Fa-ther, we thank Thee; Fa-ther in heav-en; we thank Thee.

WILLIAM W. HOW

From *Cantica Laudis*, 1850

We give Thee but Thine own, What-e'er the gift may be;

All that we have is Thine a-lone, A trust, O Lord, from Thee.

When I Pray 36

MARIE INGHAM

MARIE INGHAM

When I pray soft and low, When I pray this I know,

God will al - ways hear, God will al - ways hear.

We Thank Thee for Song

RUTH EATON WILLIAMS   D. NEIL DARNELL

Fa - ther, we thank Thee for song and for pray'r, We thank Thee for mu - sic fill - ing the air; For mel - o - dy sweet, For words to re - peat, Fa - ther, we thank Thee.

38   # We Thank Thee for Music

ANN UNDERHILL   GEORGE F. HANDEL

Fa - ther, we thank Thee, Thank Thee for mu - sic;

Mu - sic makes us joy - ful And brings us near - er to Thee.

Father, Bless Our Choir 39

Unknown   Freylinghausen's *Gesangbuch*, 1704

Fa - ther, bless our choir to - day;

Be in all we do or say, Be in ev - 'ry

song we sing, Ev - 'ry prayer to Thee we bring. A - MEN.

We Thank Thee

RALPH W. EMERSON   Old Hymn

1. For flow'rs that bloom a - bout our feet,
   For song of bird and hum of bee,

2. For blue of stream and blue of sky,
   For pleas - ant shade of branch - es high,

REFRAIN

For ten - der grass so fresh, so sweet,
For all things fair we hear or see,

For fra - grant air and cool - ing breeze,
For beau - ty of the bloom - ing trees.

Fa - ther in heav'n, we

thank Thee, Fa - ther in heav'n, we thank Thee.

41   Thank You, God, for This New Day

ELIZABETH S. WHITEHOUSE, alt.   W. LAWRENCE CURRY

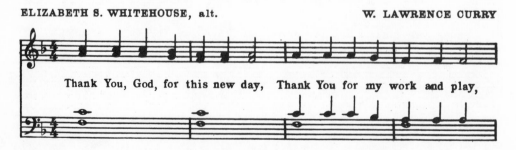

Thank You, God, for this new day, Thank You for my work and play,

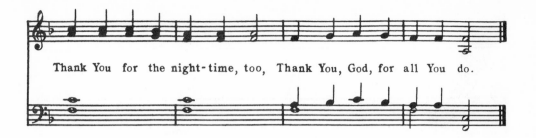

Thank You for the night-time, too, Thank You, God, for all You do.

Father, We Thank Thee for the Night 42

REBECCA J. WESTON   DANIEL BATCHELLOR

1. Fa - ther, we thank Thee for the night,
2. Help us to do the things we should,

And for the pleas-ant morn - ing light; For rest and food and
To be to oth - ers kind and good; In all we do, in

lov - ing care, And all that makes the world so fair.
work or play, To grow more lov - ing ev - 'ry day.

43

Thanks to God

ALBERT W. REAM

Brazilian Folk Song

1. In the morn - ing when I wak - en, As I
2. When at night the stars are shin - ing, Man - y

kneel and make my prayer, I give thanks to God the
chil - dren far and near Talk with God and ask His

Fa - ther, For His ten - der love and care.
bless - ing, Sleep in peace and know no fear.

44

In Jesus' Name We Pray

In Je - sus' name we pray. A - men.

He Prayeth Well

45

SAMUEL COLERIDGE TAYLOR

ROBERT LEWIS

He pray - eth well who lov - eth well Both man and bird and beast. He pray - eth best who lov - eth best All things both great and small. For the dear God who lov - eth us, He made and lov - eth all.

Hear Our Prayer

45

IRIS DEANE STARKEY

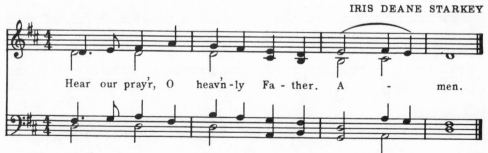

Hear our pray'r, O heav'n - ly Fa - ther. A - men.

GOD'S LOVE AND CARE

47   **The Creation**

JOHNIE B. WOOD   JOHNIE B. WOOD

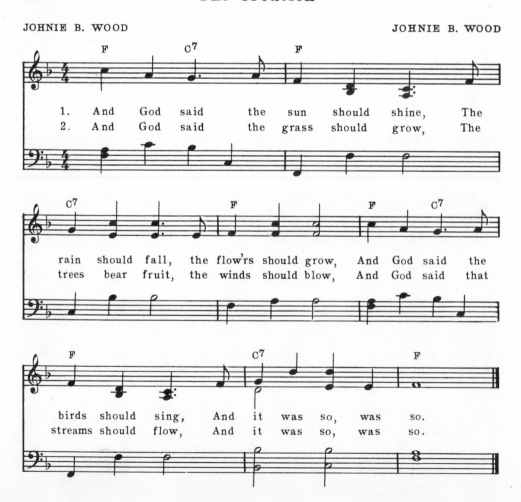

1. And God said the sun should shine, The
2. And God said the grass should grow, The

rain should fall, the flow'rs should grow, And God said the
trees bear fruit, the winds should blow, And God said that

birds should sing, And it was so, was so.
streams should flow, And it was so, was so.

God's Beautiful World

AURORA M. SHUMATE

IDA T. TRUSS

From *Songs We Sing*, copyright 1939, Broadman Press.

49   The Lord Hath Done Great Things for Us

LINA A. RAUSCHENBERG

LILLIAN ROGERS GILBREATH

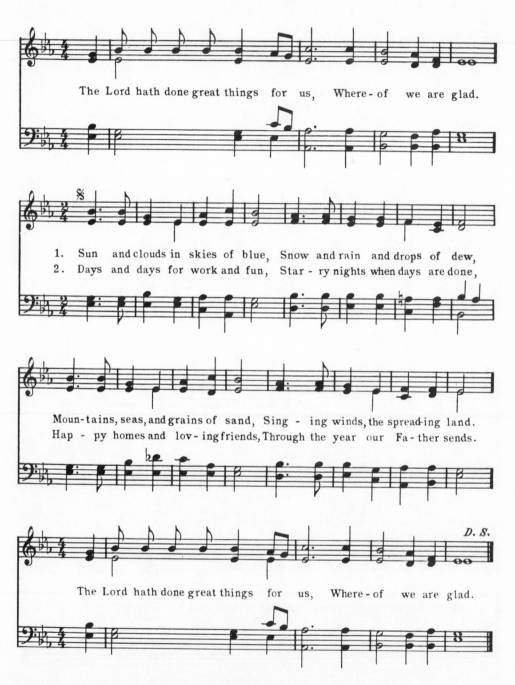

The Lord hath done great things for us, Where-of we are glad.

1. Sun and clouds in skies of blue, Snow and rain and drops of dew,
2. Days and days for work and fun, Star - ry nights when days are done,

Moun-tains, seas, and grains of sand, Sing - ing winds, the spread-ing land.
Hap - py homes and lov - ing friends, Through the year our Fa - ther sends.

D. S.

The Lord hath done great things for us, Where - of we are glad.

JOHANN WILHELM HEY
Alt. JEANNE E. SHAFFER

Welsh Melody
Arr. by ANNETTE WHEELER

1. Can you count the stars that bright-ly Twin-kle in the mid-night sky?
2. Do you know how man-y chil-dren Rise each morning bright and gay?

Can you count the clouds, so light-ly O'er the mead-ows float-ing by?
Can you count their mer-ry voic-es Sing-ing sweet-ly day by day?

God the Lord doth mark their num-ber With his eyes that nev-er slum-ber;
God hears all their hap-py voic-es, In their joy-ful songs re-joic-es;

He hath made them, He hath made them, He hath made them, ev-'ry one.
And He loves them, and He loves them, And He loves them, ev-'ry one.

God Made the Golden Sun

MARY AMBLER MARSHALL

W. LAWRENCE CURRY

God made the gold-en sun, The qui-et sil-ver rain, The

lit-tle winds that run and run A-cross the fields of grain;

Grass and buds and leaf un-curled; Ev-'ry grow-ing thing:

God made the wide and love-ly world; I make a song, and sing.

The Sun

DOROTHY SNYDER

THERESA NEWMAN

When the sun comes up each day, It comes slow - ly, on its way, Slow - ly ris - ing up so high, Up in - to the sky. When the night is com - ing near, Then the sun will dis - ap - pear, Slow - ly fall - ing in the west, While we are at rest.

God Loves Me

EDNA DEAN BAKER

Finnish Folk Song
Arr. by JANE DORSEY

Lit - tle bird and flow'r and bee Tell me that God loves me. Sun and wind and rain, all three, Tell me that God loves me. Moon and stars at night I see Tell me that God loves me.

Day Has Come and Birds Are Singing   54

NANCY BYRD TURNER

Folk Song

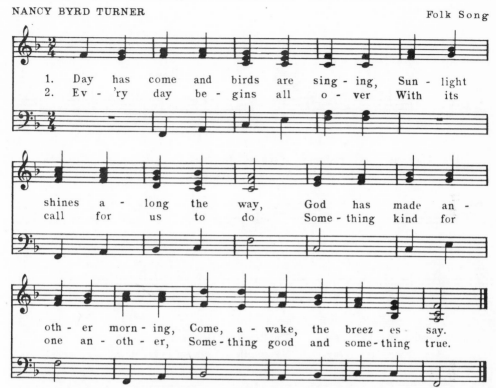

1. Day has come and birds are sing-ing, Sun-light
2. Ev-'ry day be-gins all o-ver With its

shines a-long the way, God has made an-
call for us to do Some-thing kind for

oth-er morn-ing, Come, a-wake, the breez-es say.
one an-oth-er, Some-thing good and some-thing true.

From *New Music Horizons*, Third Book, © Copyright 1953, Silver Burdett Company. Used by permission.

God Who Made the Earth   55

SARAH BETTS RHODES, stanza 1
MABEL WARKENTIN, stanza 2

JANE DORSEY

1. God who made the earth, The air, the sky, the sea,
2. God who gave my home, My par-ents, friends, and me;

Who gave the light its birth, Car-eth for me.
Who made the things I love, Car-eth for me.

From *The Church Musician*, © Copyright 1957, The Sunday School Board of the Southern Baptist Convention.

All These Things Belong to Me

Anonymous, stanza 1
MARGARET BAKER, stanza 2

MARGARET BAKER

1. The sun that shines a-cross the sea, The wind that
2. My dad who works for us each day, My friends who

whis-pers in the trees, The lark that car-ols in the sky,
wait for me to play, My moth - er smil-ing down at me,

The fleec - y clouds a-sail-ing by; Oh, I'm as
My house that holds us co - zi - ly;

rich as rich can be For all these things be - long to me!

AGNES L. MASON   PHYLLIS B. OHANIAN

1. Song birds are fly - ing a - way to the south - land, For au - tumn's here.
2. Leaves have turned gold - en and pur - ple and or - ange, For au - tumn's here.

The flow - ers have all gone to sleep un - til spring - time, For au - tumn's here.
The farm - ers are stor - ing their crops for the win - ter, For au - tumn's here.

See the Farmer Sow the Seed

FREDERICK A. JACKSON, alt.

W. G. HANCOCK, alt.

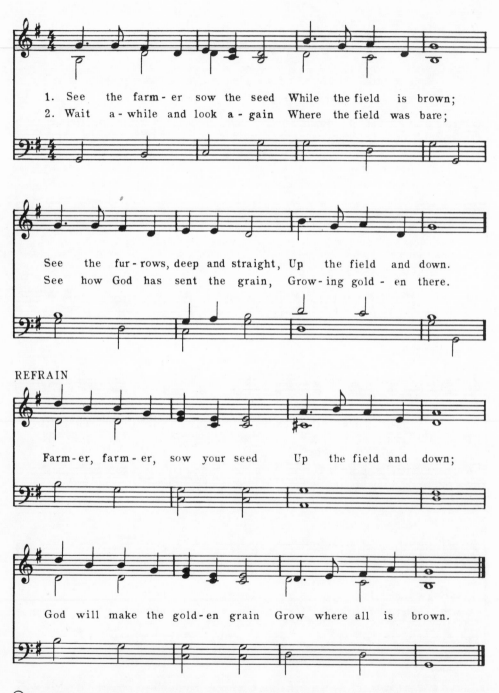

1. See   the farm-er sow the seed   While the field   is brown;
2. Wait   a-while and look a-gain   Where the field was bare;

See   the fur-rows, deep and straight, Up   the field   and down.
See   how God has sent the grain, Grow-ing gold-en there.

REFRAIN

Farm-er, farm-er, sow your seed   Up   the field and   down;

God will make the gold-en grain Grow where all   is   brown.

Back of the Loaf

MALTBIE D. BABCOCK

RUTH REED

Back of the loaf is the snow-y flour, Back of the flour the mill;

Back of the mill the wheat, the show'r, The sun, and our Fa-ther's will.

Autumn Leaves Are Now Falling

Anonymous

German Folk Tune
Arr. by MAX LYALL

1. Au-tumn leaves are now fall-ing, Red and yel-low and brown;
2. Au-tumn leaves from the tree-tops Flut-ter down to the ground;
3. Au-tumn leaves, when they're tired, In a soft hud-dled heap

REFRAIN: Tra la la la la la la, Tra la la la la la,

Au-tumn leaves are now fall-ing, See them flut-ter-ing down.
When the wind blows his trum-pet, They go whirl-ing a-round.
At the foot of the old tree, Soon will fall fast a-sleep.
Tra la la la la la la, Tra la la la la la.

Summer Days

JESSIE C. ELDRIDGE

RUTH E. WILLIAMS

Sum - mer days have man - y songs, Float - ing
on the air: Bee hums, crick - et notes,
Frog sounds, bird trills.
Sum - mer days have man - y songs That fill the
air with ech - o - ing ring Like church bells

from the dis - tant hills, dis - tant hills.

Do You Know Who Made the Night?   62

ELIZABETH McE. SHIELDS

W. LAWRENCE CURRY

1. Do you know who made the night? Made the stars and
2. Do you know who made the day? Made the glad and
3. Do you know who made the trees? Wav - ing gen - tly

moon so bright? God our Fa - ther made the night,
hap - py day? God our Fa - ther made the day,
in the breeze? God our Fa - ther made the trees,

Made the stars and moon so bright: Our Fa-ther made the night.
Made the glad and hap - py day: Our Fa-ther made the day.
Wav - ing gen - tly in the breeze: Our Fa-ther made the trees.

63 God Gave All Things

L. F. RAMSEY

B. M. RAMSEY

1. God gave all things for our pleas - ure,
2. God gave all things for our us - ing,
3. God gave all things for our liv - ing,

Flow'rs in sum - mer, win - ter's snow:
Hands to work with, hearts to love;
Health and strength and dai - ly food;

Giv - ing all in am - ple meas - ure
Left us free to do our choos - ing,
Let us thank Him for His giv - ing,

That His glo - ry we might know.
Send - ing bless - ings from a - bove.
For we know that God is good.

There Are Wonderful Things

AGNES L. MASON

PHYLLIS B. OHANIAN

1. Wher - ev - er we go there are won - der - ful things,
2.   Things we can feel like a bun - ny's smooth fur;

Bright as the col - ors on but - ter - flies' wings,
Things we can hear like a kit - ten's soft purr,

Gay as the song that a hap - py bird sings,
Things we can see like a cloud in the air,

Soft as a snow - flake that win - ter - time brings.
Won - der - ful, beau - ti - ful things ev - 'ry - where.

From *God's Wonderful World,* ⓒ copyright 1954, Agnes L. Mason and Phyllis B. Ohanian; published by The New American Library, New York. Used by permission.

65 All Good Things Around Us

MATTHIAS CLAUDIUS
Tr. by JANE M. CAMPBELL, alt.

J. A. P. SCHULZ

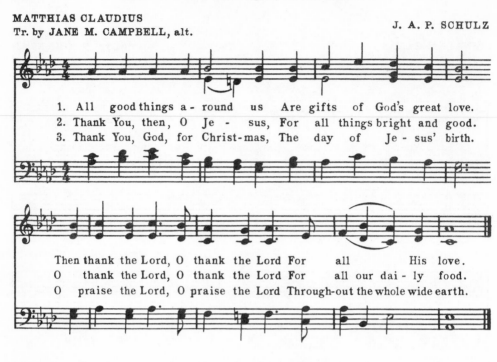

1. All good things a - round us Are gifts of God's great love.
2. Thank You, then, O Je - sus, For all things bright and good.
3. Thank You, God, for Christ-mas, The day of Je - sus' birth.

Then thank the Lord, O thank the Lord For all His love.
O thank the Lord, O thank the Lord For all our dai - ly food.
O praise the Lord, O praise the Lord Through-out the whole wide earth.

66 Gifts from Our Father

MIRIAM L. DRURY

MIRIAM L. DRURY, alt.

1. The corn and the wheat that grow in the sun, The ap-ples, and all things good,
2. The beau-ti-ful sun that shin-eth by day, The moon and the stars by night,
3. Our beau-ti-ful homes in coun-try and town, With fa-ther and moth-er there,

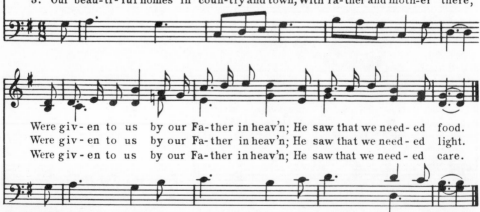

Were giv-en to us by our Fa-ther in heav'n; He saw that we need-ed food.
Were giv-en to us by our Fa-ther in heav'n; He saw that we need-ed light.
Were giv-en to us by our Fa-ther in heav'n; He saw that we need-ed care.

LIZETTE WOODWORTH REESE

GEOFFREY SHAW

Glad that I live am I; That the sky is blue;

Glad for the coun-try lanes And the fall of dew. Aft-er the sun the

rain, Aft-er the rain the sun; This is the way of

life Till the work be done. All that we need to do, Be we low or

high, Is to see that we grow near-er the sky.

Words used by permission of Estate of the late Thomas Bird Mosher and Oxford University Press. Music used by permission of Oxford University Press.

68 God's Good Gifts

LOU MONROE

LEE RODGERS

1. God gave me eyes to see His world, God gave me ears to hear,
2. All these good things that God has giv'n, I'll use them ev-'ry day

God gave my voice to sing and pray, Each time I feel Him near.
To look and lis-ten, speak and sing, To run and jump and play.

69 God, Whose Name We Love

FLORENCE HOATSON, alt.

Old English Melody

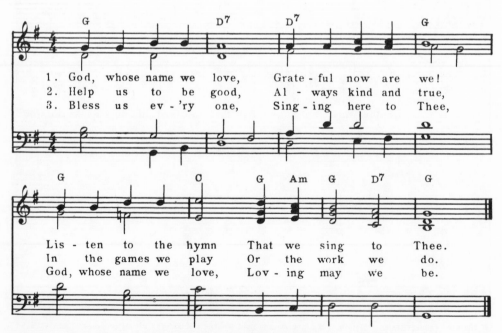

1. God, whose name we love, Grate-ful now are we!
2. Help us to be good, Al-ways kind and true,
3. Bless us ev-'ry one, Sing-ing here to Thee,

Lis-ten to the hymn That we sing to Thee.
In the games we play Or the work we do.
God, whose name we love, Lov-ing may we be.

Loving Care

NELLIE POORMAN

FRANZ SCHUBERT

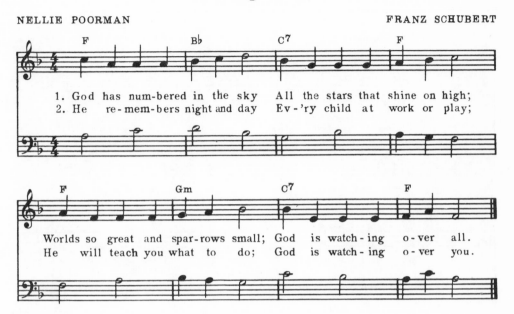

1. God has num-bered in the sky All the stars that shine on high;
2. He re-mem-bers night and day Ev-'ry child at work or play;

Worlds so great and spar-rows small; God is watch-ing o-ver all.
He will teach you what to do; God is watch-ing o-ver you.

God Is Near

ELIZABETH McE. SHIELDS, stanzas 1-4
MARY GRACE MARTIN, stanza 5

GRACE WILBUR CONANT

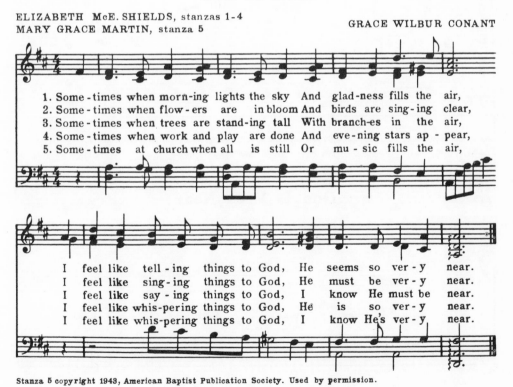

1. Some-times when morn-ing lights the sky And glad-ness fills the air,
2. Some-times when flow-ers are in bloom And birds are sing-ing clear,
3. Some-times when trees are stand-ing tall With branch-es in the air,
4. Some-times when work and play are done And eve-ning stars ap-pear,
5. Some-times at church when all is still Or mu-sic fills the air,

I feel like tell-ing things to God, He seems so ver-y near.
I feel like sing-ing things to God, He must be ver-y near.
I feel like say-ing things to God, I know He must be near.
I feel like whis-pering things to God, He is so ver-y near.
I feel like whis-pering things to God, I know He's ver-y near.

72 A Little Star Creeps O'er the Hill

ANNA M. DRAYTON, alt.

EDITH M. CASSELBERRY, alt.

A lit - tle star creeps o'er the hill,

While woods are dark and birds are still; Chil - dren think of

God's good care, And they know His love is ev - 'ry - where.

73 God Is Very Near

AURORA M. SHUMATE

HAZEL WATLINGTON

God is ver - y near; God is ver - y near;

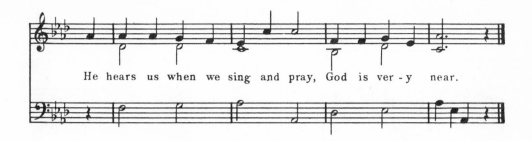

He hears us when we sing and pray, God is ver - y near.

A Prayer 74

ELSA GORHAM BAKER   IDA T. TRUSS

1. When you don't know what to do, Can't tell which way's right for you,
2. He will help you choose the way, In your work or in your play;

Pray a lit - tle prayer. You will have an an - swer true,
God is ver - y near. So if you're in doubt some day,

God will tell you what to do; God is ver - y near.
And need help to choose the way, Pray a lit - tle prayer.

75 **Evening Song**

Unknown

JEANNE E. SHAFFER

Anonymous

A. W. BINDER

1. Who taught the bird to build her nest
2. Who taught the bus - y bee to fly
3. Who taught the lit - tle ant the way
4. 'Twas God who taught them all the way,

Of wool and hay and moss?
A - mong the sweet - est flow'rs,
Its nar - row hole to bore,
And gave their lit - tle skill;

Who taught her how to weave it best,
And lay her store of hon - ey by
And thru the pleas - ant sum - mer day
He teach - es chil - dren when they pray

And lay the twigs a - cross?
To last in win - ter's hours?
To gath - er up its store?
To do His ho - ly will.

GOD SENT HIS SON

77 ## Christ Is Born

JOHNIE B. WOOD   JOHNIE B. WOOD

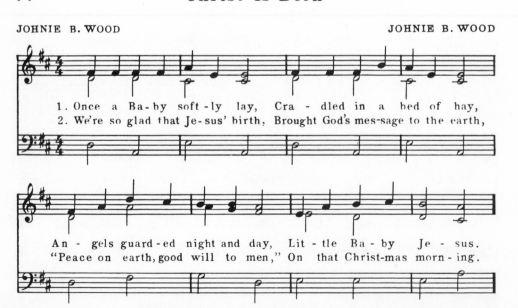

1. Once a Ba-by soft-ly lay, Cra - dled in a bed of hay,
2. We're so glad that Je-sus' birth, Brought God's mes-sage to the earth,

An - gels guard-ed night and day, Lit - tle Ba - by Je - sus.
"Peace on earth, good will to men," On that Christ-mas morn - ing.

REFRAIN

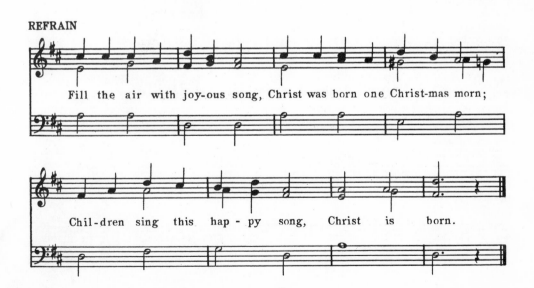

Fill the air with joy-ous song, Christ was born one Christ-mas morn;

Chil-dren sing this hap - py song, Christ is born.

Bethlehem Lay Sleeping

FRANCES B. WOOD, alt.

Polish Folk Tune
Arr. by ELLEN EASTIS

1. Beth - le - hem lay sleep - ing, Long, long a - go,
2. Shep - herds left the hill - side, Long, long a - go,
3. An - gels sweet - ly sing - ing, Long, long a - go,

Twin - kling stars were peep - ing, Long, long a - go.
Look - ing for the Ba - by, Long, long a - go.
Sent His prais - es ring - ing, Long, long a - go.

Je - sus was His name, When the Ba - by came, Long, long a - go.
Wise Men from a - far, Saw the bright - est star, Long, long a - go.
Chil - dren love did bring To the new - born King, Long, long a - go.

79

Shepherds Leave the Hillside

Anonymous

Anonymous

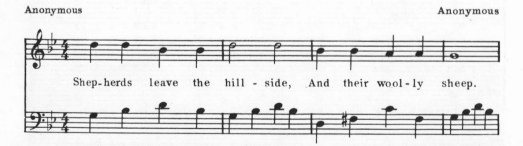

Shep - herds leave the hill - side, And their wool - ly sheep.

In a crib they find Him, Je-sus, fast a-sleep!

Christmas Lullaby

80

JEAN BOND

JEAN BOND

1. The baby Jesus in the man-ger lay,
2. The cat-tle stood a-round the man-ger bed,
3. A bright star led the Wise Men from a-far,
4. O come now, chil-dren, wor-ship, and a-dore,

Lull - a - by, Lull - a - by, The ba - by Je - sus
Lull - a - by, Lull - a - by, The cat - tle stood a -
Lull - a - by, Lull - a - by, A bright star led the
Lull - a - by, Lull - a - by, O come now, chil - dren,

in the man - ger lay, Lull - a - by, Lull - a - by.
round the man - ger bed, Lull - a - by, Lull - a - by.
Wise Men from a - far, Lull - a - by, Lull - a - by.
wor - ship, and a - dore, Lull - a - by, Lull - a - by.

81

Away in a Manger

Anonymous — JAMES R. MURRAY

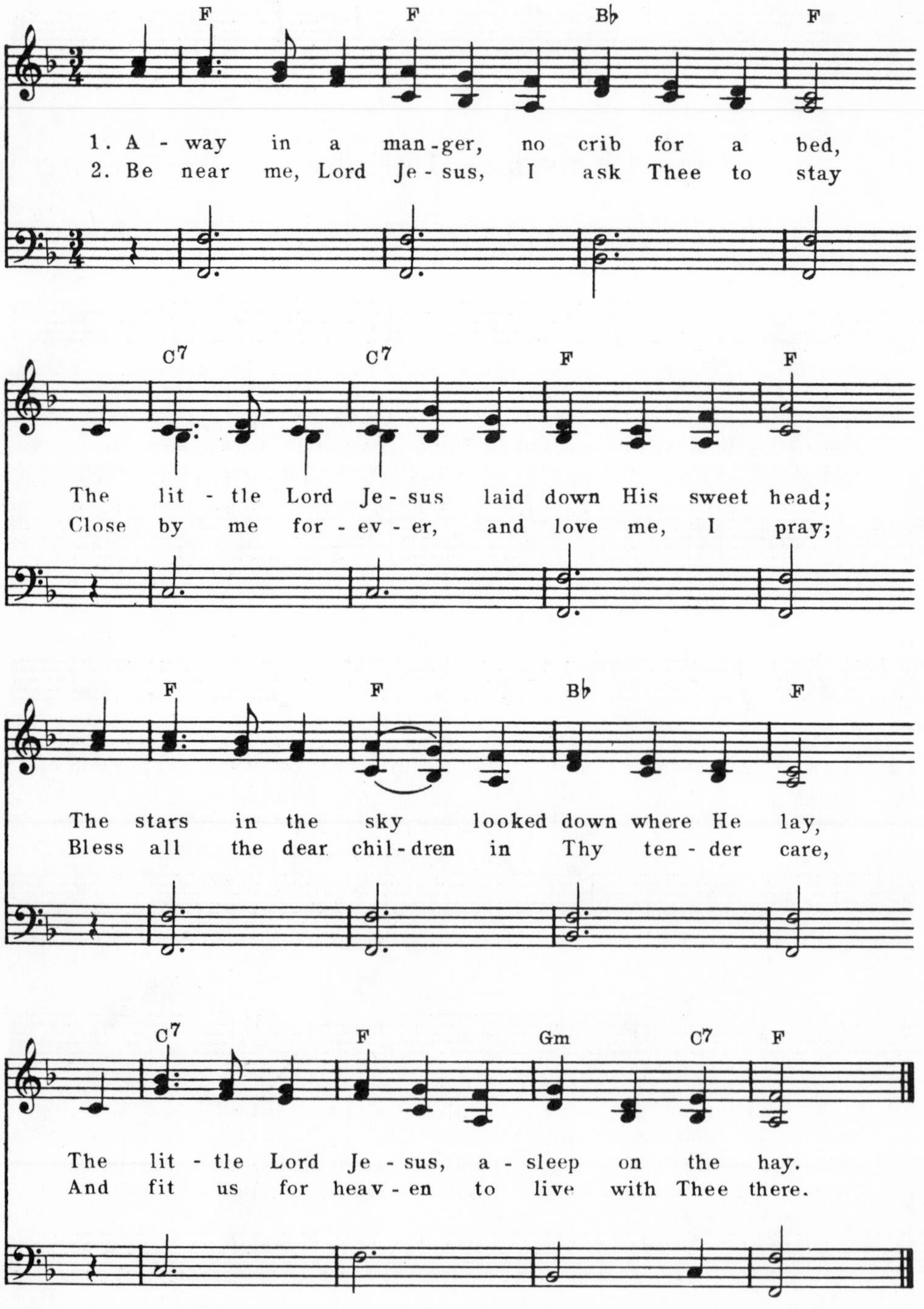

F F B♭ F
1. A - way in a man - ger, no crib for a bed,
2. Be near me, Lord Je - sus, I ask Thee to stay
C7 C7 F F
The lit - tle Lord Je - sus laid down His sweet head;
Close by me for - ev - er, and love me, I pray;
F F B♭ F
The stars in the sky looked down where He lay,
Bless all the dear chil - dren in Thy ten - der care,
C7 F Gm C7 F
The lit - tle Lord Je - sus, a - sleep on the hay.
And fit us for heav - en to live with Thee there.

Knock! Knock! Knock!

WILLIAM GRIME

WILLIAM GRIME

1. Knock, knock, knock went Jo-seph At an inn in Beth-le-hem.
2. Knock, knock, knock went Jo-seph On the sta-ble door so bright.

"Can you shel-ter a fam-i-ly And be a big help to them?"
"Can you shel-ter a fam-i-ly? For Christ shall be born to-night!"

"No room, no room," said the man in Beth-le-hem;
"Come in, come in," said the beasts of Beth-le-hem;

"No room, no room," said the man in Beth-le-hem.
"Come in, come in," said the beasts of Beth-le-hem.

Once in Royal David's City

CECIL F. ALEXANDER

HENRY J. GAUNTLETT
Arr. by JOHN HAWK

Once in roy - al Da - vid's cit - y Stood a
low - ly cat - tle shed, Where a moth - er laid her
Ba - by In a man - ger for His bed: Ma - ry
was that moth - er mild, Je - sus Christ, her lit - tle Child.

Glory to God in the Highest

(Antiphonal)

Luke 2:14

IRIS DEANE STARKEY

Glo - ry to God in the high - est!

Glo - ry to God in the high - est!

Peace on earth, Peace on earth;

Peace and good will to all men!

Timothy's Carol

WILLIAM J. REYNOLDS   WILLIAM J. REYNOLDS

The shep - herds heard the an - gels sing, The
shep - herds heard the an - gels sing. They has - tened to the
sta - ble there To wor - ship Christ the King, The
lit - tle Babe a - sleep on the hay, The lit - tle Babe a -
sleep on the hay, the hay, the hay.

Oh, Come, Little Children

Translated

JOHANN A. P. SCHULZ

1. Oh, come, lit-tle chil-dren, Oh, come, one and all,
2. Oh, see in the man-ger, In hal-low-ed light
3. Oh, there lies the Christ child, On hay and on straw;

To Beth-le-hem's sta-ble, In Beth-le-hem's stall,
A star throws its beam On this ho-li-est sight.
The shep-herds are kneel-ing Be-fore Him with awe.

And see with re-joic-ing This glo-ri-ous sight,
In clean swad-dling clothes Lies the heav-en-ly Child,
And Ma-ry and Jo-seph Smile on Him with love,

Our Fa-ther in heav-en Has sent us this night.
More love-ly than an-gels, This Ba-by so mild.
While an-gels are sing-ing Sweet songs from a-bove.

Oh, Sing a Song of Bethlehem

LOUIS F. BENSON

English Traditional Melody
Arr. by RALPH VAUGHN WILLIAMS

Oh, sing a song of Beth-le-hem, Of shep-herds watch-ing there, And of the news that came to them From an-gels in the air. The light that shone on Beth-le-hem Fills all the world to-day; Of Je-sus' birth and peace on earth The an-gels sing al-way.

Cradled upon a Bed of Hay

Anonymous

Walloon Carol
Arr. by RUTH REED

Cra - dled up - on a bed of hay, The
lit - tle Babe of Beth - l'hem in a man - ger lay; While
shep - herds watch - ing near Heard an - gel voic - es clear Sing
"Peace on earth! For Christ the Lord is born to - day."

Away in a Manger

Anonymous

WILLIAM J. KIRKPATRICK
Arr. by MAX LYALL

1. A - way in a man - ger, no crib for a bed,
2. Be near me, Lord Je - sus, I ask Thee to stay

The lit - tle Lord Je - sus laid down His sweet head;
Close by me for - ev - er, and love me, I pray;

The stars in the bright sky looked down where He lay,
Bless all the dear chil - dren in Thy ten - der care,

The lit - tle Lord Je - sus, a - sleep on the hay.
And fit us for heav - en to live with Thee there.

Jesus Lived in Naz'reth

LOU RAYMOND

LOU RAYMOND

Je - sus lived in Naz - 'reth long a - go, long a - go,

Loved the Bi - ble sto - ries long a - go, long a - go.

Je - sus grew up big and strong, Help - ing oth - ers all day long,

Je - sus lived in Naz - 'reth long a - go, long a - go.

91   **Jesus, Our Friend**

ELIZABETH McE. SHIELDS   ELDA FLETT BAKER

1. When Je - sus was a ba - by boy,
2. He helped His moth - er in the home,
3. When Je - sus grew to be a man,
4. Dear Je - sus is the chil - dren's friend;

He slept up - on the hay, And then He grew
He played like you and me: And ev - 'ry day
He made the sick ones well, And made folk good
He held them on His knee; He took them in

and worked and played Each glad and hap - py day.
He did o - bey: A hap - py boy was He.
and lov - ing by The sto - ries that He'd tell.
His arms and said, "Let chil - dren come to Me.

At Work Beside the Carpenter's Bench

ALICE M. PULLEN, alt.

English Traditional Melody

1. At work be - side the car - pen - ter's bench, At
2. And as He grew to be a man He

play when work was done; In qui - et Gal - i -
trav - el'd far and wide, To be a friend to

lee He lived, The friend of ev - 'ry - one.
all in need Through - out the coun - try - side.

Words used by permission of Alice M. Pullen.

93   We're Glad Jesus Got Home

WILLIAM GRIME   WILLIAM GRIME

1. Lis - ten   to   Ma - ry   Some-where   in   E - gypt
2. Lis - ten   to   Jo - seph   Close   by   the   don - key
3. Lis - ten— the   chil - dren   Down there   in   Naz -'reth

Sing - ing   to   Je - sus   There   as   He   slept.
Sing - ing   to   Je - sus   While   on   their   way.
Sing - ing   to   Je - sus   With   all   their   mirth.

What   is   she   sing - ing,   What   is   she   sing - ing?
What   is   he   sing - ing,   What   is   he   sing - ing?
What   are they   sing - ing,   What   are they   sing - ing?

I'll   be   so   glad   when   we   can   go   home.
I   am   so   glad   that   we're   go - ing   home.
We   are   so   glad   that   Je - sus   got   home.

Jesus Lived in a Little House

WILLIAM GRIME

WILLIAM GRIME

1. Je - sus lived in a lit - tle house
2. Je - sus lived in a lit - tle house
3. Je - sus lived in a lit - tle house
4. Je - sus lived in a lit - tle house

Where there was lots to do,
Where there was lots to do,
Where there was lots to do,
Where there was lots to do,

Like roll - ing up the sleep - ing mats
Like grind - ing meal for dai - ly bread
Like get - ting wa - ter from the well
Like sweep - ing floors till coins were found

And fill - ing oil lamps, too.
And learn - ing les - sons, too.
And feed - ing pi - geons, too.
And clean - ing san - dals, too.

Jesus Was a Loving Teacher

WILHELMINA D'A. STEPHENS

CHARLOTTE A. BARNARD

1. Je - sus was a lov - ing teach - er,
Help - ing peo - ple day by day Know the love of
God our Fa - ther, Teach - ing them to love and pray.

2. Je - sus was a pa - tient teach - er,
Want - ing all to learn God's will, Tell - ing sto - ries
they'd re - mem - ber—Sto - ries that we're read - ing still.

3. God, we thank Thee for this teach - er,
And our praise to Thee we give, For His love and
for His pa - tience, Show - ing peo - ple how to live.

96 Jesus, Friend of Little Children

WALTER J. MATHAMS

MARTIN SHAW

1. Je - sus, friend of lit - tle chil - dren, Be a friend to me:
2. Teach me how to grow in good - ness, Dai - ly as I grow:

Care for me and ev - er keep me Close to Thee.
Thou hast been a child, and sure - ly Thou dost know.

The Children's Friend   97

JESSIE ELEANOR MOORE   HELEN H. LEMMEL

1. Long a - go the lit - tle chil - dren
2. Come and lis - ten to the sto - ry,

Gath - ered close to Je - sus' knee, For His kind - ly
Friend of chil - dren still is He, Lis - ten then and

smile said gen - tly, "I love them and they love Me."
whis - per soft - ly, "I love Him and He loves me."

Jesus Loves Me

ANNA B. WARNER

WILLIAM B. BRADBURY

Je-sus loves me! this I know, For the Bi-ble tells me so;

Lit-tle ones to Him be-long; They are weak, but He is strong.

REFRAIN

Yes, Je-sus loves me, Yes, Je-sus loves me,

Yes, Je-sus loves me, The Bi-ble tells me so.

Spanish:

    Chris-to me a-ma,
    Chris-to me a-ma,
    Chris-to me a-ma,
    La Bib-lia di-ce a-si.

Chinese:

    Ju Ye-su nai wo,
    Ju Ye-su nai wo,
    Ju Ye-su nai wo,
    Shung jing i ko ru wo.

Japanese:

    Wa ga Shu E-su,
    Wa ga Shu E-su,
    Wa ga Shu E-su,
    Wa-re wo a-i-su.

Italian:

    Si Je-su m'a-ma,
    Si Je-su m'a-ma,
    Si Je-su m'a-ma,
    La Bib-lia me la di-ce.

ELSIE G. RODGERS

NETTIE LOU JONES

1. The lov - ing Je - sus is my friend; His
2. One day He said, "All those who love— Who
3. Some-times it seems so ver - y hard To

qui - et voice speaks in my heart; He helps me choose what's
do not quar - rel, but are kind, Who help each oth - er
be po - lite, and kind, and true; And then I whis - per

right to do, And makes me brave to do my part.
and for - give— I glad - ly call each one My friend."
to my - self, "You're Je - sus' friend; He counts on you."

100 Come, Ye Children, Sing to Jesus

FRANCIS SMITH   MARIE INGHAM

1. Come, ye chil - dren, sing to Je - sus, On this hap - py
2. Sing, ye chil - dren, sing to Je - sus, Sing His prais - es

East - er Day. Christ our Sav - iour now is ris - en,
sweet and clear. All the earth is filled with glad - ness,

Let His lit - tle chil-dren say. All the bells are glad-ly ring - ing,
Tell the chil-dren ev -'ry-where. All the bells are glad-ly ring - ing,

All the flow'rs are gai - ly spring - ing,
All the flow'rs are gai - ly spring - ing,

All the birds with joy are sing - ing;
All the birds with joy are sing - ing;

Come, ye chil - dren, praise and pray.
Come, ye chil - dren, praise and pray.

101 ## Once There Was a Garden Fair

NANCY BYRD TURNER, alt. ROBERTA BITGOOD

1. Once there was a gar-den fair, Far a-way a-
2. Je-sus' grave was guard-ed well Through the dark-ness
3. Some-thing great and pow-er-ful In that gar-den

cross the sea. Some-thing pow-er-ful and great Hap-pened
deep and lone, But be-fore the morn-ing broke An-gels
far a-way Hap-pened for the whole wide world On the

there for you and me, Al - le-lu - ia! Al-le-lu - ia!
rolled a - way the stone, Al - le-lu - ia! Al-le-lu - ia!
first great East-er Day, Al - le-lu - ia! Al-le-lu - ia!

102 ## On This Happy Easter

GRACE STORMS TOWER EVELYN E. MURRAY

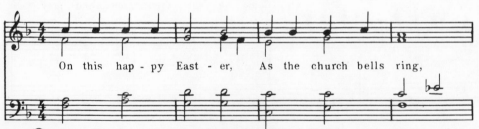

On this hap-py East-er, As the church bells ring,

Chil-dren tell of Je-sus' love And al-le-lu-ias sing.

A Song for Easter   103

BEATRICE PERHAM KRONE

Bohemian Melody
Arr. by JANE DORSEY

1. Dark and gloom have passed a-way, Al-le-lu-ia. Bright the dawn on
2. Let the earth re-joice and sing, Al-le-lu-ia. Joy to all this

East-er Day, Al-le-lu - ia. Al-le-lu - ia,
day will bring,

Al-le-lu - ia. Christ is ris-en, Al-le-lu - ia.

104   ## For Stories Fine and True

ETHEL L. SMITHER

GEORGE F. ROOT

We thank Thee, O our Fa - ther, For sto-ries fine and true

Of peo-ple in the Bi - ble Who knew and loved Thee, too.

They learned to serve Thee brave - ly, To help 'gainst pain and wrong;

They won-dered at Thy good - ness; They praised in joy-ous song.

Words used by permission of author.

NANCY BYRD TURNER   GRACE WILBUR CONANT

The Word of God shall guide my feet, Wher-ev-er I may go; The Word of God will teach to me The things I ought to know; The Word of God will make me strong And bless me through my whole life long, And bless me through my whole life long.

The Bible Is the Best Book

JOHNIE B. WOOD

JOHNIE B. WOOD

1. The Bi-ble is the best book, A book that is so dear— A
2. The Bi-ble, too, has let-ters That bring good news in them, The

sto-ry book, a pic-ture book, A book of songs that cheer; The
Bi-ble tells us Je-sus said Let chil-dren come to Him; The

Bi-ble tells of Je-sus, Who came from heav'n a-bove; The
Bi-ble has good les-sons On what a child should be; The

Bi-ble brings the mes-sage sweet That God is love.
Bi-ble is a book from God For you and me.

Unknown

Melody from *Heilige Seelenlust,* 1657

1. My Bi - ble! 'Tis a book di - vine,
2. My Bi - ble! In this book a - lone

Where heav'n - ly truth and mer - cy shine,
I find God's ho - ly will made known;

And wis - dom speaks in ev - 'ry line,
And here His love to man is shown,

And speaks to me, And speaks to me.
His love to me, His love to me.

108   # The Bible Is a Treasure Book

ELIZABETH McE. SHIELDS, stanza 1
SUE L. WHATLEY, stanza 2

SUE L. WHATLEY

1. The Bi-ble is a treas-ure book Of sto-ries that are true;
2. The Bi-ble is a song-book, too, For out of Psalms we know

It tells of peo-ple long a-go, Of folks like me and you.
Come songs of pray'r and songs of praise, Our Fa-ther's love to show.

109   # Holy Bible, Book of Love

EVONE WOOD CAPELL

IRVING WOLFE

1. Ho-ly Bi-ble, book of love, Tell me of our God a-bove.
2. Ho-ly Bi-ble, here I read Of God's laws that I should heed.
3. Ho-ly Bi-ble, once a-gain Tell of God's great love to man—
4. Ho-ly Bi-ble, book of love, Tell me of the home a-bove;

He who made me loves me still, Helps me know and do His will.
Help me strong-er, pur-er grow, And God's love to oth-ers show.
How He gave His on-ly Son, How Christ died for ev-'ry-one.
Of the place pre-pared for me, Where with Christ I can ev-er be.

This Is the Day Which the Lord Hath Made   110

Psalm 118:24

MIRIAM L. DRURY

This is the day which the Lord hath made; We will re-joice,

Interlude   We will re-joice and be glad in it.

O Give Thanks   111

Psalm 107:1

RUTH REED

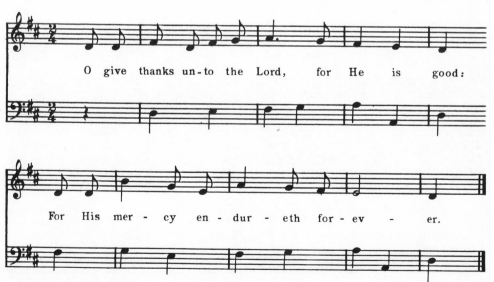

O give thanks un-to the Lord,   for He is   good:

For His mer - cy en - dur - eth for - ev - er.

112   Lo, the Winter Is Past

Song of Solomon 2:11, 12   EDWARD SHIPPEN BARNES

Lo, the win-ter is past; The rain is
o-ver and gone; The flow'rs ap-pear on the
earth; The time of the sing-ing of birds is come.

The Earth Is Full of the Love of the Lord   113

Based on Psalm 33:5

IRVING WOLFE

The earth is full of the love of the Lord. The love-ly sky, the

birds that fly, And the songs that make our hearts sing to Him; The

joy of life, all grow-ing things, And the smiles that shine when

we love the Lord. The earth is full of the love of the Lord.

114 **He That Is Faithful**

Luke 16:10

ROBERTA HADLEY
Harmonized by REBA DAWSON

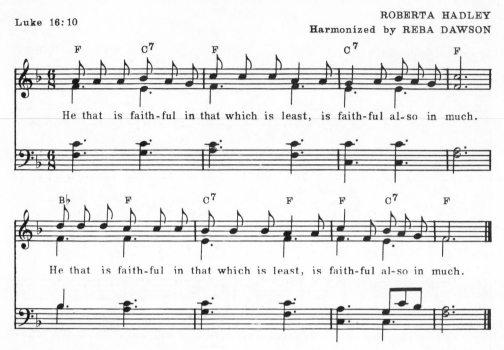

He that is faith-ful in that which is least, is faith-ful al-so in much.

He that is faith-ful in that which is least, is faith-ful al-so in much.

115 **Bring Thank Offerings**

2 Chronicles 29:31

ETHEL V. WILLIAMS

Bring thank of-f'rings, bring thank of-f'rings in-to the house of the Lord.

Bring thank of-f'rings, bring thank of-f'rings in-to the house of the Lord.

I Am with Thee and Will Keep Thee 116

Genesis 28:15

LEE RODGERS

"I am with thee, and will keep thee," God told Ja-cob long a - go,

God is with us and will keep us Wher-ev-er we may go.

Give Thanks 117

Psalm 118:1

GERALDINE E. MUCHMORE

Give thanks un-to the Lord, Give thanks un-to the Lord,

Oh! give thanks un-to the Lord, For He is good.

Psalm 100

(Unison)

From Psalm 100

JANE M. MARSHALL

Make a joy-ful noise un-to the Lord, all ye

lands. Serve the Lord with glad - ness:

come be - fore His pres - ence with sing - ing.

En - ter His gates with thanks - giv - ing,

and His courts, His courts with praise:

Make a joy-ful noise un-to the Lord,

all ye lands.

If Ye Love Me 119

John 14 : 15
Matthew 28 : 20

IRIS DEANE STARKEY

Je-sus said, "If ye love Me, keep My com-mand-ments,

If ye love Me, keep My com-mand-ments." And He said,

"Lo, I am with you, Lo, I am with you." He will help me, I know.

120 As Ye Would that Men Should Do to You

Luke 6:31

ETHEL V. WILLIAMS

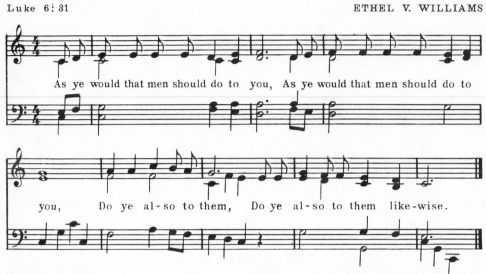

As ye would that men should do to you, As ye would that men should do to
you, Do ye al-so to them, Do ye al-so to them like-wise.

From *Primary Teacher*, Copyright 1950, The Sunday School Board of the Southern Baptist Convention.

121 Be Kind

Ephesians 4:32

IRVING WOLFE

Be kind to one an-oth - er, ten-der-heart-ed, for-
giv-ing one an-oth - er; for-giv - ing, for-giv - ing, for-
giv-ing one an-oth - er. Be kind to one an-oth-er.

When David Was a Shepherd Boy

SUE L. WHATLEY

D. W. DEARLE

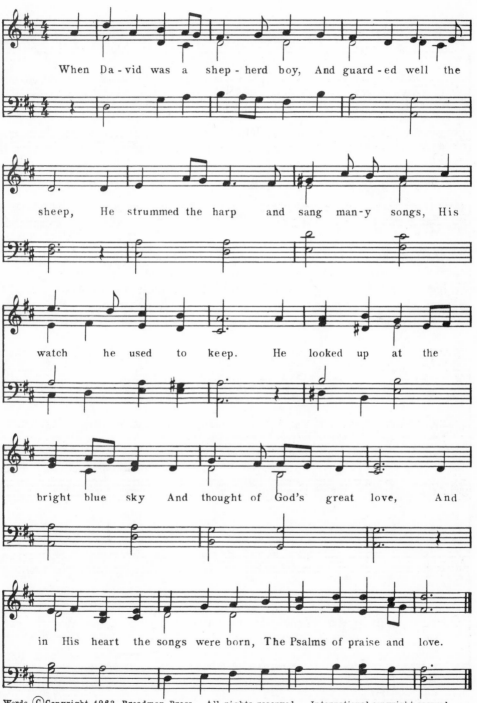

When Da-vid was a shep-herd boy, And guard-ed well the sheep, He strummed the harp and sang man-y songs, His watch he used to keep. He looked up at the bright blue sky And thought of God's great love, And in His heart the songs were born, The Psalms of praise and love.

123

Miriam

JEAN BOND JEAN BOND

1. Long a - go a lit - tle girl named Mir - iam
2. When the prin - cess heard the ba - by cry - ing,
3. Then she ran and brought the ba - by's moth - er.

Watched her ba - by broth - er ev - 'ry day.
She said, "Go and bring the child to me."
She said, "I will care for him each day."

He was in a lit - tle bas - ket cra - dle;
Mir - iam asked if she should get a nurse - maid
God was kind and saved the ba - by Mo - ses,

In this lit - tle bed He had to stay.
Who would feed and treat him lov - ing - ly.
And they thanked Him when they knelt to pray.

Paul and Silas

JEAN BOND   JEAN BOND

1. Paul and Si - las sang in a pris - on,
2. Al - ways preach - ing, al - ways prais - ing,

Songs of praise both night and day.
Prais - ing God and His own Son,

An an - gel came and o - pened the gates, Then
While oth - ers learned to share their glad - ness,

Paul and Si - las went on their way.
Know - ing Je - sus loves ev - 'ry - one.

THE CHURCH

125   We Love Our Church, O God

NAN F. HEFLIN, stanza 1
CLARA BEERS BLASHFIELD, stanza 2

AARON WILLIAMS

1. We love our church, O God, We love to gath-er here
2. We love our church, O God, This place of friend-ly cheer;

To wor-ship, work, and learn of Thee With Chris-tian friends so dear.
We come to sing, to work, to pray To God who is ev-er near.

EDITH LOVELL THOMAS, stanza 1
MABEL WARKENTIN, stanza 2

CHARLES F. GOUNOD
Arr. by **FRANCIS DAY**

1. Glad - ly to the house of wor - ship come we to - day,
2. We give thanks and praise to God who gives us the day,

Thanks to give for qui - et church - es where peo - ple pray;
And for all our dai - ly needs we come here to pray;

For the or - gan mu - sic sound - ing far off and near;
While the preach - er reads the Bi - ble, God's word we hear;

For the high, sun - light - ed win - dows, col - ored or clear.
When our wor - ship hour is o - ver, God still is near.

127   Dear God, We Like to Come to Church

MARY GRACE MARTIN

Scottish Psalter, 1615

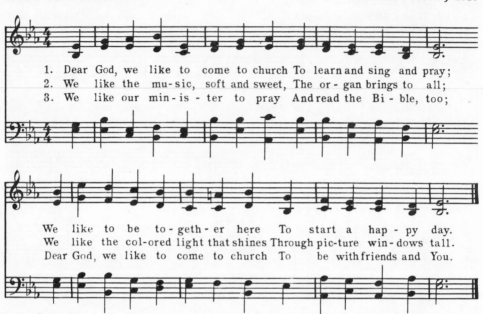

1. Dear God, we like to come to church To learn and sing and pray;
2. We like the mu-sic, soft and sweet, The or-gan brings to all;
3. We like our min-is-ter to pray And read the Bi-ble, too;

We like to be to-geth-er here To start a hap-py day.
We like the col-ored light that shines Through pic-ture win-dows tall.
Dear God, we like to come to church To be with friends and You.

128   When in the Quiet Church I Sit

ESTHER FREIVOGEL

JOHN B. DYKES

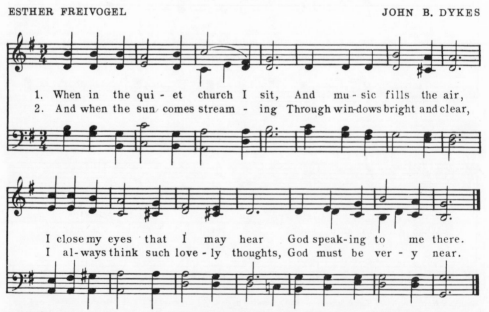

1. When in the qui-et church I sit, And mu-sic fills the air,
2. And when the sun comes stream-ing Through win-dows bright and clear,

I close my eyes that I may hear God speak-ing to me there.
I al-ways think such love-ly thoughts, God must be ver-y near.

NELL I. MINOR and
EMILY BRYANT

IRVING WOLFE

I love to wor-ship in our church With friends and fam'-ly

dear, And when we bow our heads in prayer We feel God ver-y

near. I thank You, God, that You have planned That peo-ple in this

way, Shall come to-geth-er in our church To

think and sing and pray. I love to wor-ship in our church.

130 Surely the Lord Is in This Place

JUANITA H. WILSON   JUANITA H. WILSON

"Sure-ly the Lord is in this place." He will hear us
as we praise Him; "Sure-ly the Lord is in this place."
Let us pray and sing praise un-to Him. A - MEN.

131 At Church

JUANITA H. WILSON   JUANITA H. WILSON

I will lis-ten care-ful-ly To each word that's said;
I will lis-ten prayer-ful-ly When God's Word is read.

Our Church Helps Us to Worship God   132

MABEL NIEDERMEYER   CHARLES STEGGALL

1. Our church helps us to wor - ship God; We
2. The Bi - ble sto - ries that we learn Help

sing our songs of praise, And talk with Him in qui - et tones
us to know God's care. They tell of Je - sus and His friends

And work in friend - ly ways. We feel that God is
And show us how to share. We feel that God is

ver - y near As we work and wor - ship here.
ver - y near As we work and wor - ship here.

MISSIONS

133 The Whole World Is Singing

MARGARET BAKER   MARGARET BAKER

1. The whole world is sing-ing, Chil - dren sing-ing to-
2. The whole world is sing-ing, Chil-dren who live in this

geth - er raise Songs of hap-pi-ness, love and praise,
world with me, What-ev - er your race or lan-guage may be,

The whole world is sing-ing, Sing-ing to Christ, the King.
Come join in our sing-ing, Sing-ing to Christ, the King.

Jesus Loves the Children

134

Anonymous

LEE RODGERS

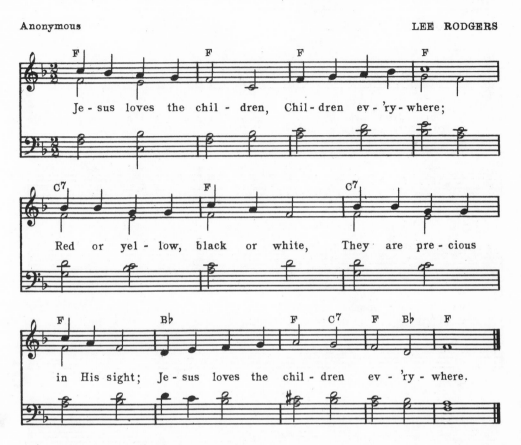

Je - sus loves the chil - dren, Chil - dren ev - 'ry - where;

Red or yel - low, black or white, They are pre - cious

in His sight; Je - sus loves the chil - dren ev - 'ry - where.

135 Children Who Live Across the Sea

WILLIAM GRIME

WILLIAM GRIME

1. Chil - dren who live a - cross the sea,
2. Chil - dren who pray a - cross the sea,
3. Chil - dren who work a - cross the sea,

What - e'er your race or col - or be,
What - e'er your race or col - or be,
What - e'er your race or col - or be,

Let us to - geth - er sing our praise
Let us to - geth - er kneel and say,
Let us to - geth - er try to make

To God our Fa - ther all our days.
"Our Fa - ther, bless each one to - day."
A bet - ter world, for Je - sus' sake. A - MEN.

Children of Other Lands

ALAN GRAY M. CAMPBELL   ALAN GRAY M. CAMPBELL

1. In oth-er lands a-cross the sea, Are man-y chil-dren
2. In coun-tries near, and coun-tries far, Wher-ev-er lit-tle

just like me; And I must help to tell them there, That
chil-dren are, We need to make them un-der-stand That

REFRAIN

Je - sus' love is ev-'ry-where. For Je - sus loves the
He loves those of ev-'ry land.

chil - dren A - cross the wa - ters blue. If they

do not know, we must tell them so; Then they will love Him, too.

137

We Will Share the Sweet Stories

MATTIE C. LEATHERWOOD

MILDRED ADAIR STAGG

We will share the sweet sto - ries of Je - sus

With chil - dren who live far and near;

He loves them, too, and the sto - ries true,

He wants all the chil - dren to hear.

THE HOME

We Thank Thee, Father, for Our Homes   138

ELIZABETH McE. SHIELDS

Arr. from a German Folk Song
Arr. by CALVIN W. LAUFER

We thank Thee, Fa-ther, for our homes; For friends who help each day; For food we eat and clothes we wear; For all the gifts Thy chil-dren share; For work and rest and play.

139 Our Home

Anonymous

JANE DORSEY
Arr. by MAX LYALL

1. Our home is such a hap - py place,
2. Our home is such a hap - py place,

We're bus - y all the day;
The nic - est place I know:

There's so much work for us to do,
We work to - geth - er ev - 'ry day

So man - y games to play.
To help to make it so.

ANNETTE WHEELER   ANNETTE WHEELER

God, bless our home with love and joy,

Give us Thy peace and ten - der care,

Bless our fam' - ly, bless our neigh - bors,

Bless our home, O God, we pray.

141   He Is Near Me

LOIS H. YOUNG   LOIS H. YOUNG

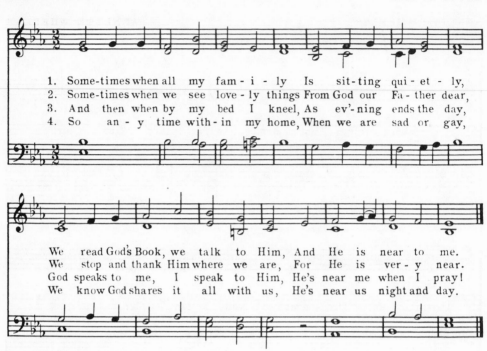

1. Some-times when all my fam - i - ly Is sit-ting qui - et - ly,
2. Some-times when we see love - ly things From God our Fa - ther dear,
3. And then when by my bed I kneel, As ev'-ning ends the day,
4. So an - y time with-in my home, When we are sad or gay,

We read God's Book, we talk to Him, And He is near to me.
We stop and thank Him where we are, For He is ver - y near.
God speaks to me, I speak to Him, He's near me when I pray!
We know God shares it all with us, He's near us night and day.

142   My Father and My Mother

LOUISE M. OGLEVEE   WILLIAM G. OGLEVEE

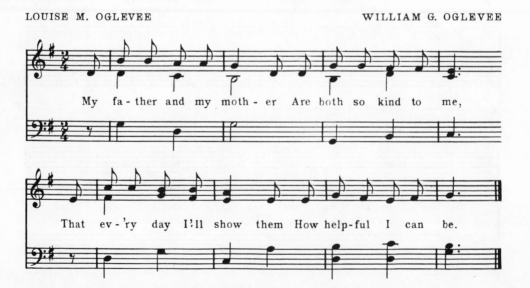

My fa - ther and my moth - er Are both so kind to me,

That ev - 'ry day I'll show them How help-ful I can be.

I Give Thanks 143

FRANCES McKINNON MORTON

RUTH BAMPTON

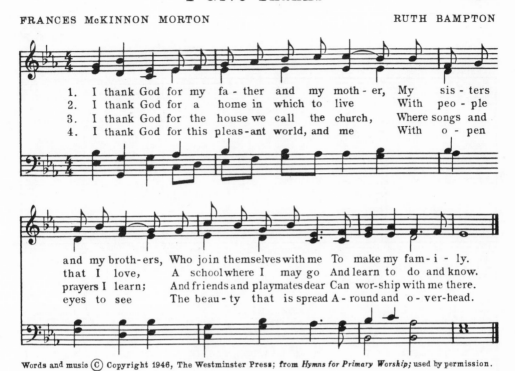

1. I thank God for my fa-ther and my moth-er, My sis-ters
2. I thank God for a home in which to live With peo-ple
3. I thank God for the house we call the church, Where songs and
4. I thank God for this pleas-ant world, and me With o-pen

and my broth-ers, Who join themselves with me To make my fam-i-ly.
that I love, A school where I may go And learn to do and know.
prayers I learn; And friends and playmates dear Can wor-ship with me there.
eyes to see The beau-ty that is spread A-round and o-ver-head.

House Blessing 144

ARTHUR GUITERMAN

LOU ADAMS

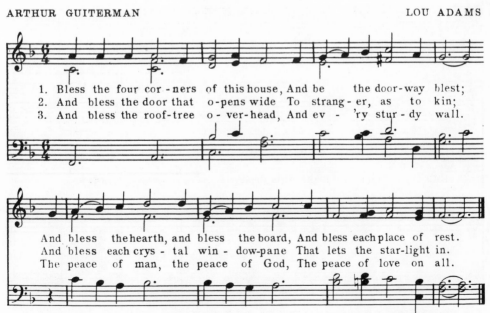

1. Bless the four cor-ners of this house, And be the door-way blest;
2. And bless the door that o-pens wide To strang-er, as to kin;
3. And bless the roof-tree o-ver-head, And ev-'ry stur-dy wall.

And bless the hearth, and bless the board, And bless each place of rest.
And bless each crys-tal win-dow-pane That lets the star-light in.
The peace of man, the peace of God, The peace of love on all.

How I Love My Home

Southern Folk Song
Arr. by CHARLES F. BRYAN

How I love my home, sweet home! How I love my

home, sweet home, How I love my home, sweet home, For my

moth - er⎱
fa - ther⎰ helps to make this beau - ti - ful home.
sis - ter
broth - er helps to make this beau - ti - ful home.

CALVIN W. LAUFER

EDWARD SHIPPEN BARNES

1. When twi-light falls the birds fly home, Each to his
2. So fa-thers from their work re-turn, And chil-dren

down-y nest, And while the stars shine
from their play, To find that home's the

o-ver-head They fold their wings and rest.
dear-est spot Where one can come and stay.

GROWING

147 I Can Grow

JESSIE B. CARLSON   JESSIE B. CARLSON

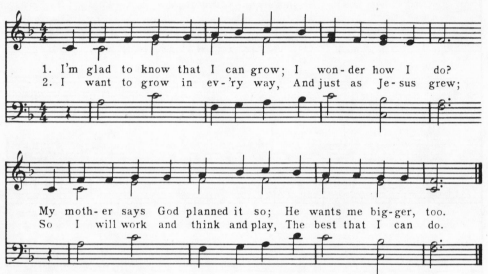

1. I'm glad to know that I can grow; I won-der how I do?
2. I want to grow in ev-'ry way, And just as Je-sus grew;

My moth-er says God planned it so; He wants me big-ger, too.
So I will work and think and play, The best that I can do.

From *Home and Church Songs,* © Copyright 1958, Christian Board of Publication. Used by permission.

148 I Want to Be Like Jesus

SALLIE FUTRELL STONE   SALLIE FUTRELL STONE

Ev-'ry day, ev-'ry day, I want to be like Je-sus;

When I work, when I play, I want to be like Je-sus.

HATTIE BELL ALLEN   HATTIE BELL ALLEN

1. I want to be help-ful and lov-ing, At home and at school and at play. I wish I could be just like Je - sus, He all of God's rules did o - bey.

2. At home He was al - ways o - be - dient, As ev - 'ry good child ought to be; He shared ev - 'ry task that was set Him, When He was a child just like me.

3. He grew like the oth - ers a - round Him; He went to the syn - a-gogue school; He stud - ied His les - sons and learned them, Was care - ful to keep ev - 'ry rule.

4. When He played on the green, grass - y hill - sides With the boys and the girls as they came, He tried to be thought-ful of oth - ers, And kept ev - 'ry rule of the game.

5. I wish I could grow just like Je - sus! I'll ask Him to help, and I can, "In - creas - ing in wis - dom and stat - ure, And in fa - vor with God and man."

Je - sus, Je - sus, I want to be just like Him.

150   Growing Like Jesus

JOHN JOSEY   JANE M. MARSHALL

I wish I had known the boy Je - sus In His
home, at His work, at His play. I know He was lov - ing and
kind and good, And help - ful to some - one each day. I'm
glad that I know a - bout Je - sus Who
hears me each time that I pray. I want to grow more and more

like Him In all that I do ev-'ry day.

Glad I Am to Grow!   151

ELIZABETH McE. SHIELDS   FLORENCE JOLLEY

1. Glad I am to live! Glad I am to grow!
2. Glad I am to live! Glad I am to grow!

I would grow as Je-sus grew, Strong in bod-y, strong to do
Fa-ther, may each com-ing day Make me strong to do Thy way

What is right and brave and true. Glad I am to grow!
As I work and as I play. Glad I am to grow!

152   How to Grow

N. FLORENCE LEECH

JANE DORSEY

1. I feed my bod - y with whole - some food, I
2. I feed my mind when I stud - y, Love

ex - er - cise and play; Be - cause I want to grow
fills my heart when I pray; I'm grow - ing in mind, in

big and strong, In ev - 'ry sort of way.
bod - y and soul, Ev - 'ry sin - gle day.

153   Pleasing God

DORIS MONROE

FRANZ SCHUBERT

1. God is pleased each time I say, "Thank You, God, for this glad day;
2. God is pleased each time I read Sto - ries from the Bi - ble true;
3. God is pleased each time I use Sun - day as a day of rest—

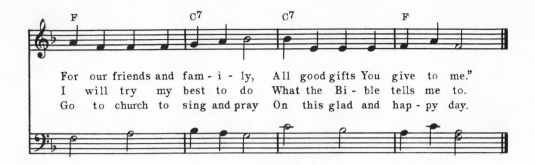

For our friends and fam - i - ly, All good gifts You give to me."
I will try my best to do What the Bi - ble tells me to.
Go to church to sing and pray On this glad and hap - py day.

I Would Follow Jesus

154

FRANK VON CHRISTIERSON

German Folk Song
Arr. by ROBERTA BITGOOD

I would fol - low Je - sus — Teach - er, Friend, and Guide;

In my work and in my play, In my home and school each day,

In God's world so fair and wide, I would fol - low Je - sus.

FRIENDS AND NEIGHBORS

155   **Friends of Jesus**

NANCY BYRD TURNER   RUTH REED

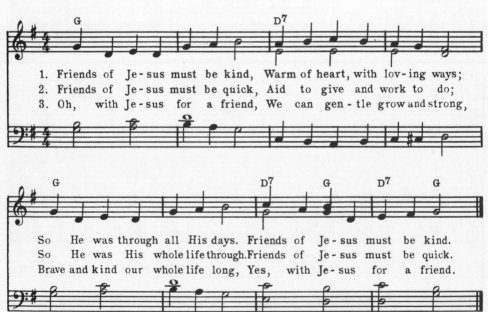

1. Friends of Je-sus must be kind, Warm of heart, with lov-ing ways;
2. Friends of Je-sus must be quick, Aid to give and work to do;
3. Oh, with Je-sus for a friend, We can gen-tle grow and strong,

So He was through all His days. Friends of Je-sus must be kind.
So He was His whole life through. Friends of Je-sus must be quick.
Brave and kind our whole life long, Yes, with Je-sus for a friend.

MILDRED HAMMON MILDRED HAMMON

A friend lov-eth at all times, When things are good or bad. A friend lov-eth at all times, Re-joic-eth when we're glad. A friend help-eth in trou-ble, A friend is al-ways true; A friend lov-eth at all times, A friend I'll be to you.

157   My Best Friend Is Jesus

MILDRED ADAIR STAGG   MILDRED ADAIR STAGG

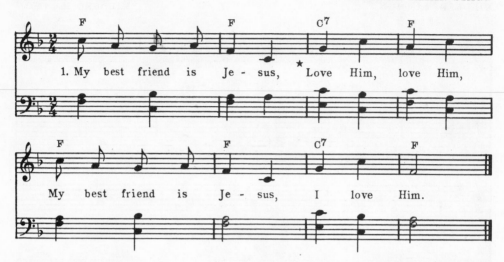

1. My best friend is Je - sus, ★ Love Him, love Him,

My best friend is Je - sus, I love Him.

★ 2. Thank Him
3. Praise Him
4. Serve Him

From *Songs We Sing*, Copyright 1939, Broadman Press. All rights reserved.

158   Friends Who Help Us

RUTH REED   RUTH REED

1. There are man - y peo - ple who help us ev - 'ry day,

★ The post-man brings our mail,   1. He's a friend of mine.
church, 2-6. All are friends of mine.

★ 2. The policeman at the corner,
3. The milkman at the door,
4. The grocer at the store,
5. The boy who brings our paper,
6. The pastor at our church,

I Love My Friends and They Love Me   159

CALVIN W. LAUFER   W. HINES SIMS

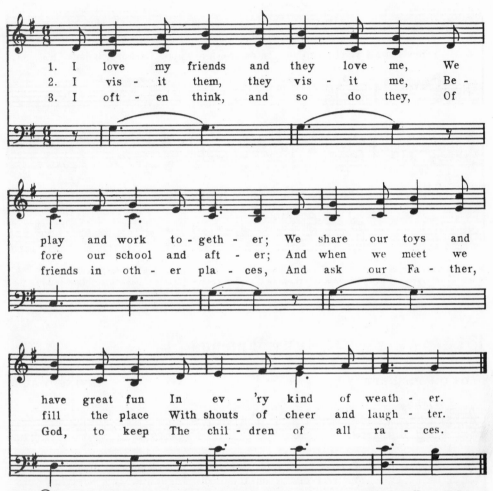

1. I love my friends and they love me, We
2. I vis - it them, they vis - it me, Be -
3. I oft - en think, and so do they, Of

play and work to - geth - er; We share our toys and
fore our school and aft - er; And when we meet we
friends in oth - er pla - ces, And ask our Fa - ther,

have great fun In ev - 'ry kind of weath - er.
fill the place With shouts of cheer and laugh - ter.
God, to keep The chil - dren of all ra - ces.

160   Friends of All We'd Like to Be

ELIZABETH McE. SHIELDS   JANE DORSEY

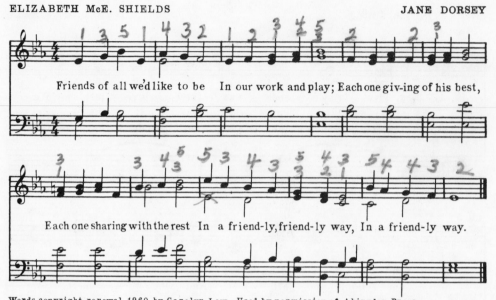

Friends of all we'd like to be   In our work and play; Each one giv-ing of his best,

Each one sharing with the rest   In a friend-ly, friend-ly way, In a friend-ly way.

161   My Friends

BLOSSOM BENNETT   IRVING WOLFE

Brightly

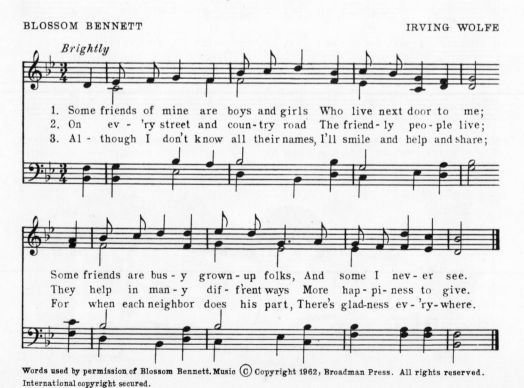

1. Some friends of mine are boys and girls Who live next door to me;
2. On ev - 'ry street and coun-try road The friend-ly peo-ple live;
3. Al - though I don't know all their names, I'll smile and help and share;

Some friends are bus - y grown-up folks, And some I nev-er see.
They help in man - y dif-f'rent ways More hap-pi-ness to give.
For when each neighbor does his part, There's glad-ness ev-'ry-where.

Friends

JEAN CONDER SOULE

JANE M. MARSHALL

How nice to have a play-mate true! How good to have a friend To bring you joy; to share a toy; To bor-row or to lend. How won-der-ful to call by name A dear friend, kind and true; And bet-ter still, through God's own will, To know that friend is you.

163   Friends! Friends! Friends!

ELIZABETH McE. SHIELDS, alt.

ELIZABETH McE. SHIELDS
Arr. by MAX LYALL

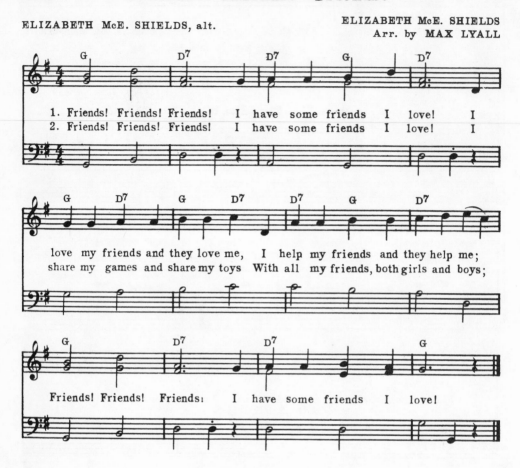

1. Friends! Friends! Friends! I have some friends I love! I
2. Friends! Friends! Friends! I have some friends I love! I

love my friends and they love me, I help my friends and they help me;
share my games and share my toys With all my friends, both girls and boys;

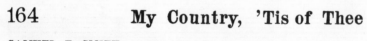

Friends! Friends! Friends! I have some friends I love!

PATRIOTIC

164   My Country, 'Tis of Thee

SAMUEL F. SMITH

Anonymous

1. My coun - try, 'tis of thee, Sweet land of lib - er - ty,
2. My na - tive coun - try, thee, Land of the no - ble free,
3. Let mu - sic swell the breeze, And ring from all the trees
4. Our fa - thers' God, to Thee, Au - thor of lib - er - ty,

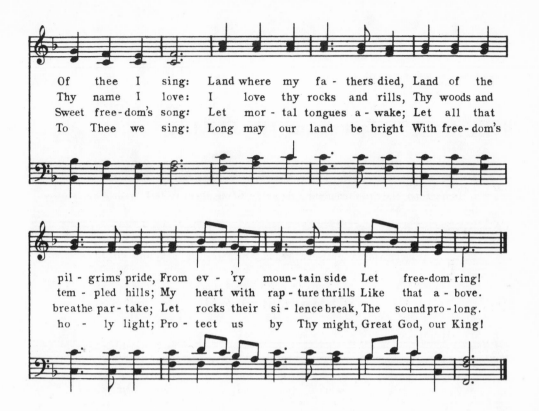

Of thee I sing: Land where my fa - thers died, Land of the
Thy name I love: I love thy rocks and rills, Thy woods and
Sweet free-dom's song: Let mor - tal tongues a - wake; Let all that
To Thee we sing: Long may our land be bright With free-dom's

pil - grims' pride, From ev - 'ry moun-tain side Let free-dom ring!
tem - pled hills; My heart with rap - ture thrills Like that a - bove.
breathe par - take; Let rocks their si - lence break, The sound pro - long.
ho - ly light; Pro - tect us by Thy might, Great God, our King!

To America   165

RUTH BAMPTON   Adapted from HAYDN

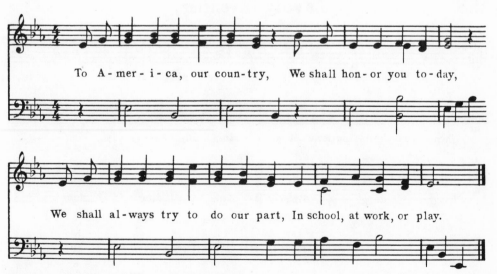

To A - mer - i - ca, our coun-try, We shall hon - or you to - day,

We shall al - ways try to do our part, In school, at work, or play.

ROUNDS

166 Jesus and the Children

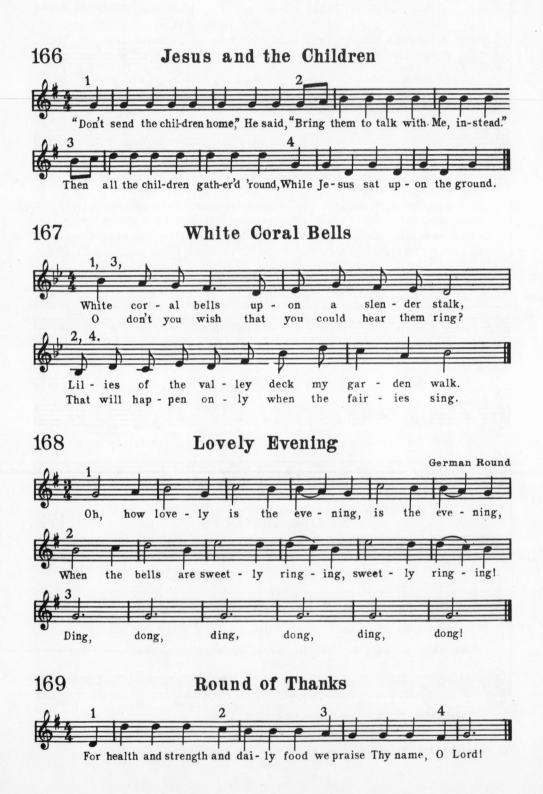

"Don't send the chil-dren home," He said, "Bring them to talk with Me, in-stead."

Then all the chil-dren gath-er'd 'round, While Je-sus sat up-on the ground.

167 White Coral Bells

1, 3,
White cor-al bells up-on a slen-der stalk,
O don't you wish that you could hear them ring?

2, 4.
Lil-ies of the val-ley deck my gar-den walk.
That will hap-pen on-ly when the fair-ies sing.

168 Lovely Evening

German Round

Oh, how love-ly is the eve-ning, is the eve-ning,

When the bells are sweet-ly ring-ing, sweet-ly ring-ing!

Ding, dong, ding, dong, ding, dong!

169 Round of Thanks

For health and strength and dai-ly food we praise Thy name, O Lord!

Come, Let Us Gather

Traditional Round

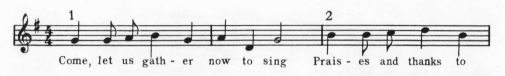

Come, let us gath - er now to sing Prais - es and thanks to

God our King. God's love is great - er than an - y - thing.

Praise and Thanksgiving

Alsatian Round

Praise and thanks - giv- ing let ev-'ry-one bring Un- to our

Fa - ther for ev-'ry good thing! All to-geth - er joy-ful- ly sing.

Praise the Lord

BILL F. LEACH

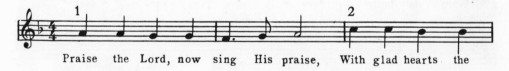

Praise the Lord, now sing His praise, With glad hearts the

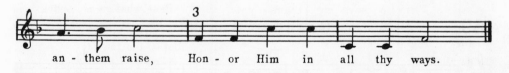

an - them raise, Hon - or Him in all thy ways.

FUN AND FOLK SONGS

173   **Young Musicians**

German Game Song

Melody: Autoharp, Melody Bells, or Song Bells

1-3.0 I'm a young mu- si- cian, I like to play a tune.

Triangle or Bells:

Rhythm Sticks:

Tambourine:

Vi - o - lin I'm play - ing, Lis-ten what it's say - ing:
Trum - pet I'm play - ing, Lis-ten what it's say - ing:
Drum I am play - ing, Lis-ten what it's say - ing:

Dee - dle dum dum dum, dee - dle dum dum dum,
Toot - a - too too too, toot-a - too too too,
Rub - a - dub dub dub, rub-a - dub dub dub,

So says my vi - o - lin.
So says my trum - pet.
So says my drum - ming.

4. O we are young musicians,
     We make a jolly band;
All of us are playing,
     Hear what we are saying:
Deedle dum dum dum,
     deedle dum dum dum,
Toot-a-too too too,
     rub-a-dub dub dub,
All making music.

★ Introduction only.

How I Love to Sing

ELLEN EASTIS

ELLEN EASTIS

La la la la, How I love to sing,

La la la la, How I love to sing,

La la la, la la la, La la la la la!

La la la la, How I love to sing.

Planting Rice

Filipino Folk Song

Plant-ing rice is nev-er fun; Bent from morn till set of sun. Can-not stand and can-not sit; Can-not rest for a lit-tle bit. Plant-ing rice is no fun; Bent from morn till set of sun. Can-not stand, can-not sit; Can-not rest for a lit-tle bit.

The Green Dress

Tr. by JOSEPH MARAIS

Folk Song from South Africa

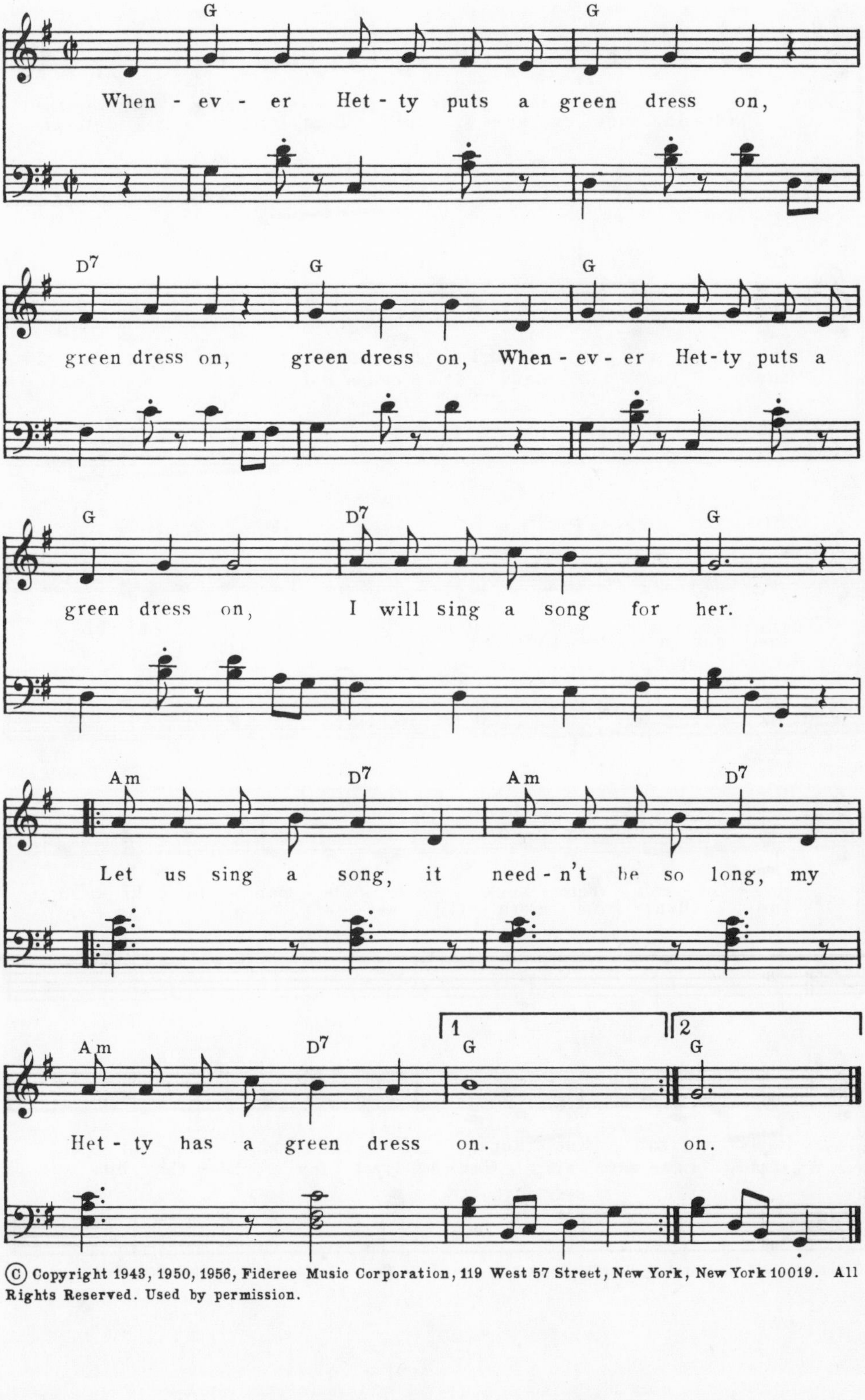

G G
When - ev - er Het - ty puts a green dress on,
D7 G G
green dress on, green dress on, When - ev - er Het - ty puts a
G D7 G
green dress on, I will sing a song for her.
Am D7 Am D7
Let us sing a song, it need - n't be so long, my
Am D7 1 G 2 G
Het - ty has a green dress on. on.

Kuckuck — Cuckoo

English by KATHERINE F. ROHRBOUGH

Austria

Oh, I went to Pe-ter's flow-ing spring Where the wa-ter's so good; And I heard there the cuc-koo As she called from the wood. Ho - li - ah, Ho - le-rah - hi-hi - ah, Ho - le - rah Kuc - kuck. Ho - le - rah - hi - hi - ah, Ho - le - rah Kuc - kuck. Ho - le - rah - hi - hi - ah,

Ho - le - rah Kuc-kuck. Ho - le - rah - hi-hi - ah - ho.

Before Dinner

CAROL HART SAYRE

Congo Children's Song
Arr. by CAROL HART SAYRE

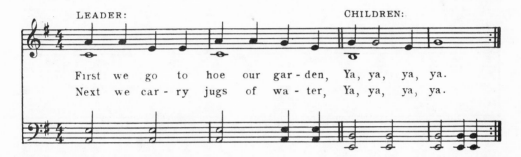

LEADER: CHILDREN:

First we go to hoe our gar-den, Ya, ya, ya, ya.
Next we car-ry jugs of wa-ter, Ya, ya, ya, ya.

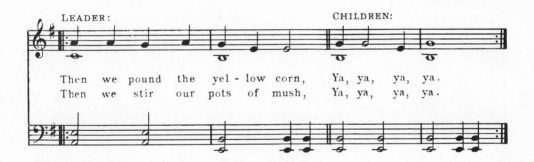

LEADER: CHILDREN:

Then we pound the yel-low corn, Ya, ya, ya, ya.
Then we stir our pots of mush, Ya, ya, ya, ya.

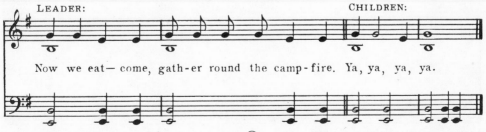

LEADER: CHILDREN:

Now we eat— come, gath-er round the camp-fire. Ya, ya, ya, ya.

From *The Whole World Singing* by Edith Lovell Thomas, Ⓒ Copyright 1950, Friendship Press. Used by permission.

Counting Song

English by LUCILLE WOOD

Mexican Children's Song

Spanish: U - no, dos y tres, cua - tro, cin - co, seis,

Sie - te, o - cho, nue - ve, I can count to diez.

★ Instruments

La la la la la, La la la la la,

La la la la la la; la.

★ Instruments: claves or sticks, maracas or gourds, drums, guiro, cabaca.

Clap Your Hands

RUTH REED

RUTH REED

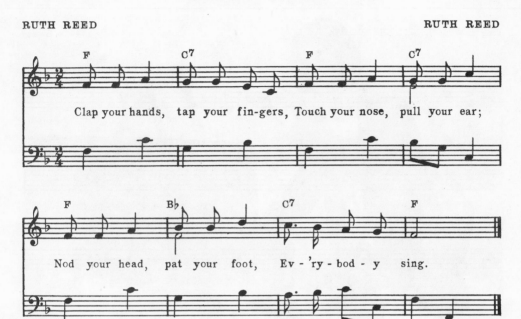

Clap your hands, tap your fin-gers, Touch your nose, pull your ear;

Nod your head, pat your foot, Ev-'ry-bod-y sing.

Who Is Sitting Next to You?

RUTH REED

RUTH REED

Who is sit-ting next to you, Sing-ing mer-ri-ly and

bright? On your right, (clap, clap, clap,) on your

right, (clap, clap, clap,) Won't you please tell us his name?
(her)

182

Opening theme from the *Pastoral Symphony (The Messiah)*

GEORGE F. HANDEL

183

Theme from *And My Spirit Hath Rejoiced (The Magnificat)*

JOHANN S. BACH
Arr. by MAX LYALL

Theme from the *Andante, Symphony in G*

JOSEPH HAYDN

Theme from the *Rondo, Sonata in A, K. 331*

WOLFGANG A. MOZART
Arr. by MAX LYALL

Lively

186

186

Theme from *Wie bist du meine Königin*

JOHANNES BRAHMS
Arr. by MAX LYALL

Chorale theme from Fourth Movement, *Symphony No. 9*

LUDWIG VAN BEETHOVEN
Arr. by MAX LYALL

Theme from *O Rest in the Lord (Elijah)*

FELIX MENDELSSOHN
Arr. by MAX LYALL

Topical Index

(Titles are in small caps; first lines in lower case type)

FRIENDS AND NEIGHBORS

A friend loveth at all times, 156
As ye would that men should do to you, 120
Be kind, 121
Day has come and birds are singing, 54
FRIENDS, 162
Friends! Friends! Friends! 163
Friends of all we'd like to be, 160
Friends of Jesus, 155
FRIENDS WHO HELP US, 158
How nice to have a playmate true! 162
I love my friends and they love me, 159
My best friend is Jesus, 157
MY FRIENDS, 161
Some friends of mine are boys and girls, 161
The loving Jesus is my friend, 99
There are many people who help us, 158

FUN AND FOLK SONGS

Autumn leaves are now falling, 60
BEFORE DINNER, 178
Bethlehem lay sleeping, 78
Clap your hands, 180
COUNTING SONG, 179
Day has come and birds are singing, 54
First we go to hoe our garden, 178
GOD LOVES ME, 53
Hallelujah! 9
How I love my home, 145
HOW I LOVE TO SING, 174
I would follow Jesus, 154
In the morning when I waken, 43
KUCKUCK-CUCKOO, 177
La la la la, how I love to sing, 174
Little bird and flower and bee, 53
O I'm a young musician, 173
Oh, I went to Peter's flowing spring, 177
Planting rice, 175
THANKS TO GOD, 43
Thanksgiving time has come, 32
THE GREEN DRESS, 176
Uno, dos y tres, 179
We thank Thee, Father, for our homes, 138
Whenever Hetty puts a green dress on, 176
Who is sitting next to you? 181
YOUNG MUSICIANS, 173

GOD SENT HIS SON

Easter

A SONG FOR EASTER, 103
Come, ye children, sing to Jesus, 100
Dark and gloom have passed away, 103
On this happy Easter, 102
Once there was a garden fair, 101

Jesus and the Children

"Don't send the children home," He said, 166
JESUS AND THE CHILDREN, 166
Jesus, friend of little children, 96
Jesus loves the children, 134
JESUS, OUR FRIEND, 91
Jesus was a loving teacher, 95
Long ago the little children, 97
THE CHILDREN'S FRIEND, 97
When Jesus was a baby boy, 91

Jesus' Birth (Christmas, Special Days)

Away in a manger, 81
Away in a manger, 89
Bethlehem lay sleeping, 78
CHRIST IS BORN, 77
CHRISTMAS LULLABY, 80
Cradled upon a bed of hay, 88
Glory to God in the highest, 84
Knock! knock! knock! 82
Oh, come, little children, 86
Oh, sing a song of Bethlehem, 87
Once a Baby softly lay, 77
Once in royal David's city, 83
Shepherds leave the hillside, 79
The baby Jesus in the manger lay, 80
The shepherds heard the angels sing, 85
TIMOTHY'S CAROL, 85

Jesus' Childhood

At work beside the carpenter's bench, 92
Jesus lived in a little house, 94
Jesus lived in Naz'reth, 90
JESUS, OUR FRIEND, 91
Listen to Mary somewhere in Egypt, 93
WE'RE GLAD JESUS GOT HOME, 93
When Jesus was a baby boy, 91

Jesus' Love

At work beside the carpenter's bench, 92
I am so glad, 29
Jesus loves me, 98
JESUS, OUR FRIEND, 91
Jesus was a loving teacher, 95
My best friend is Jesus, 157
The loving Jesus is my friend, 99
When Jesus was a baby boy, 91

GOD'S LOVE AND CARE

God's Gifts

All good things around us, 65
ALL THESE THINGS BELONG TO ME, 56
GIFTS FROM OUR FATHER, 66
Glad that I live am I, 67
God gave all things, 63
God gave me eyes to see His world, 68
GOD'S GOOD GIFTS, 68

*Index of Songs with Autoharp Markings

(Titles are in small caps; first lines in lower case type)

*The autoharp markings are for playing the autoharp only. Do not play the autoharp when playing the piano accompaniment.

Index of First Lines and Titles

(Titles are in small caps; first lines in lower case type)

158